THE EVOLUTION OF THE MACHINE

THE EVOLUTION OF THE MACHINE

by RITCHIE CALDER

Consultant
EUGENE S. FERGUSON
Professor of Mechanical Engineering
Iowa State University

Published by **AMERICAN HERITAGE PUBLISHING CO., INC.**
in association with **THE SMITHSONIAN INSTITUTION**

Book trade and institutional distribution by
D. VAN NOSTRAND COMPANY INC.

CONTENTS

This volume inaugurates a new series, marking a collaboration between American Heritage and the Smithsonian Institution. Few partnerships could be more appropriate, for American Heritage has a splendid tradition in publishing studies on the history of this country for the reading public, while the Smithsonian, for more than a hundred years, has been gleaning and collating aspects of America, its science, history, and art. It is planned that the series will be on science, and particularly the natural sciences.

As many readers will know, the motto of our Institution is, "for the increase and diffusion of knowledge among men." In 1846, the year of the Institution's founding, Professor Joseph Henry, the first Secretary of the Smithsonian, was busy jotting down notes for future policy. His leather-bound notebook lies before me.

"It should be recollected," he wrote, "that our government is merely the trustee of the will of (James) Smithson, and since his object is to increase and diffuse knowledge among men, the benefits of its (the Institution's) operations should be as widely spread as possible . . ."

Publish, disseminate widely. These were primary concerns of Henry, and they have been followed ever since by the Smithsonian, often in concert with publishing firms.

For the first time the destiny of the whole earth seems within man's grasp. Science and technology have leaped forward at man's bidding, as this first book in the series dramatically illustrates. So today the future is intertwined with man's inventions in a new and novel way. The series will attempt to make the intelligent reader see more of the world for what it is, and his place in that world. In every case the relation between the volumes and some aspect of the Smithsonian storehouse will be apt, as one tends to elucidate the other. It is our sincere hope that the series will more than justify our partnership, and will indeed increase and diffuse knowledge among men.

S. Dillon Ripley

PREFACE

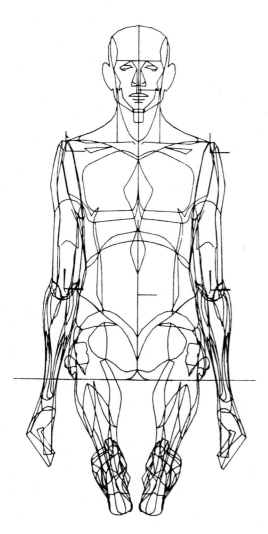

This computer-drawn sketch depicts the body structure of an average Air Force pilot. It is part of a new technique called computer graphics, which designers currently use to solve complex visual problems.

Speaking before the 1959 International Conference on Information Processing, in Paris, Dr. Edward Teller shocked his audience with the following: "If you give a machine a large enough memory and give it enough random trials, it will remember those trials which are successful. It will thus learn. I believe that the machine can be given the power to make value judgments and from that I can construct, mathematically, a model for machine-emotion."

Professor Teller was giving this "kiss of life" to the machine before a group that included engineers, mathematicians, logicians, physiologists, and philologists. Of the more than two thousand participants only a fraction were involved with machines that we generically label "electronic computers," and which had been first used only fourteen years previously. And yet they already represented a billion dollar industry. Following his remark about "machine-emotions," I stood up and asked whether machines would ever make love. His studied, tongue in cheek reply was, "Yes—dispassionately!" Although this was only banter in the discussions, we did hear later about machines throwing tantrums and having nervous breakdowns when stupid humans gave them the wrong sort of information. We also heard how computers could correct mistakes and memorize the incident for future reference—a form of learning; how that learning would automatically be built into the next generation of computers—a form of inherited experience; how computers could design computers and control the machines that manufactured computers—a form of breeding; how machines could not only translate existing languages but even create their own—a language not of literacy but of numeracy; how machines could compose music as distinctive as the call signs of a bird; how they could recognize and memorize patterns and pass them on to their machine progeny, like the instinct that makes a chick scurry to cover when it sees the shadow of a hawk; and how computers, from their accumulated experience, could memorize laws and invent machines that human beings had not even contemplated. While Teller's electronic "take-over bid" was being enthusiastically expounded, one veteran computer-man loudly interrupted: "Thank God for power failures!"

What does The Machine, deified with capital letters, mean to each of us? To some zealots at the Paris convention it meant the computer. To some it is just the "one-armed bandit" of the gambling casino. It can be a high-powered automobile or a rocket blasting off Cape Kennedy at an incredible velocity. It can be a supersonic jet, a pencil sharpener, a giant earthmover, or a communications satellite relaying television pictures from the other side of the globe. It may also be an automatic shoe cleaner competing with a shoeshine-boy, or a completely automated factory doing the work of hundreds of workers. In more grandiloquent terms, it can be The Great Liberator of human drudgery. But it can also be the monster of Doctor Frankenstein's genius.

A century ago Charles Darwin wrote *The Descent of Man* as a sequel to his momentous *The Origin of Species*, in which he propounded his theory of evolution. He scandalized the orthodox by tracing man's ancestry back to the ape. This book will be an attempt to trace the descent of the machine, although the computer aristocracy may not recognize their ancestry in the Acheulian hand ax. It begins with our ancestral apes coming down out of the trees and standing erect as the first toolmaking animal. The roots of the machine's genealogical tree are in the brain of this conceptual man, capable of ideas and of translating them into artifacts by those finger skills that differentiated him from all other creatures. After all, it was he who made the machine.

Three hundred years ago a machine was defined as "an apparatus for applying mechanical power consisting of a number of parts, each having a definite function," but a more appropriate description (to make it consistent with electronics, in which the "parts" are atomic particles) would be "any arrangement for taking in some definite form of energy, modifying it, and delivering it in a form more suitable for the desired purpose." This applies to any type of machine, whether it is a lever transferring muscle-energy, a windmill grinding corn, a nuclear generating station transferring the energy of the atom to transmission lines, geothermal stations using energy extracted from volcanic structures, or magneto-hydrodynamic generators removing electricity directly from superheated gases. This diversity explains why a good deal of our attention must be devoted to energy sources and their conversion, without which the entire "machine" concept becomes somewhat meaningless.

Also indispensable to machines are materials, whether naturally available or artificially contrived. For example the Eskimos, historically, did not produce machines that had moving parts. Yet I know (having lived with them) that the Eskimos are ingenious, deft-fingered, and skilled with blueprint, photographic memories (innate after four thousand years of pinpoint navigation across the wastes of the snow barrens). I knew a boy at Aklavik, at the mouth of the Mackenzie River, who was given a watch for his birthday and instantly did what many boys would have done—take it apart. When the school bell rang for prayers he stuffed the parts into his cap and rammed it in his parka pocket; the next day, from memory, he put it together again. This exceptional talent explains why Canadian authorities are now training Eskimos as watchmakers and precision engineers for modern electronics. But why then did they develop no technoculture? Because the only materials readily accessible to them were stone and ice. No "family tree" of machines would be complete, therefore, without an understanding of the collateral branches of materials, metals, and, more recently, the development of plastics.

Since the time of Darwin, biologists have learned about the genes, chromosomes, and "mutations" that determine or change heredity. Similarly, there have been "inherited" characteristics in the evolution of the machine. Techniques have often been handed down without modification. Where they have persisted their origins will be recalled and their "inheritance" traced. But what changed the ape into man were "mutations." In the evolution of the machine these were the points of sudden departure that depended on imagination and conceptual thought.

A machine, by any definition, consists of parts working together. To understand the evolution of the machine we must take into account their anatomy—how the parts were invented, how they were adapted, and what is their contemporary relevance.

As in the evolution of all animate things there is an "ecology" for mechanical things, that is, surrounding circumstances that either encouraged or discouraged developments. In the case of the machine the ecology was mainly social and economic. For instance when slaves could be acquired by making wars, dominant civilizations had plenty of muscle-power and thus little need for laborsaving devices to do their work. Another example of an ecological factor was the conjunction of neighboring coal and iron that coincided with the improvement of the steam engine to give Britain its initial advantage in the Industrial Revolution. For similar "ecological" reasons (apart from the military or political consequences of the atom bomb) the Manhattan Project demands our consideration; it was the first of the major "crash programs" that, by producing a shotgun wedding of science and technology, hurtled us unexpectedly into the Atomic Age; it programmed us into the Cybernetic Age (with computers and automation), and rocketed us into the Space Age. Each of these ages was as epochal as the Iron Age, the Bronze Age or the

Industrial Revolution; and it is staggering to think that all were conceived within the lifetime of a child born in 1945. If we do not grasp the significance of the "crash program" we will not realize the new time scale in the evolution of the machine.

Another factor in the rapid acceleration of new machines is the universality of communications—the press, radio, television, and rapid transportation. Until recently inventions and processes took a long time to diffuse. Sometimes they were discovered independently at different places and at different times. Often many centuries separated the appearance of an invention in one place and its reappearance somewhere else. For example the standard method of interconversion of rotary and longitudinal motion—the eccentric cam, the connecting rod, and the piston rod assembly—was widely used in China by 970 A.D., but it did not appear in Europe until the fifteenth century. Sometimes it was just a matter of remoteness, at other times it was deliberate. The Indian smiths of Hyderabad had a monopoly on a secret process for making fine steels which they exported profitably to the West to be made into Damascene and Toledo blades. But they shipped it through Ethiopia so that its origins would not be known. Here was an early example of industrial secrecy. Today many industrial concerns have elaborate security arrangements to prevent spies from discovering trade secrets before they can be patented. But it is only a short-term (though profitable) advantage. Since scientific principles are universal new discoveries can usually be traced back to their scientific origins; very often they also prompt other ideas. Publication and communication in professional societies bring about rapid interchange and application. Traditional obstacles to progress, like the gas industry's struggle against electricity in the last century, no longer prevail.

In the evolution of the machine man is the creator. It is he who gets an idea and he who puts it to work. In recent years the isolated inventor has become the exception. More and more invention has become the result of teamwork and even market research—finding out what the customer is likely to want and inventing accordingly. That is why special attention will be paid to Edison and the electric lamp. His Menlo Park experiment was the beginning of the modern "research factory"; it had the domestic lamp, as individual as a candle, as its predetermined goal.

In the sweep of history the subject of the machine is vast. This book will attempt to trace that process of selection by which the bits and pieces that constitute our contemporary machines came together.

What we are witnessing today is a speeded up process—like those films that illustrate before one's eyes the entire process by which a seed becomes a beautiful flower. More great discoveries and inventions (drastically changing our lives) have occurred in the last fifty years, and particularly the past twenty-five, than in all previous history of mankind. As an enthusiastic physicist recently said: "Today, we are privileged to sit side-by-side with the giants on whose shoulders we stand."

SURVIVAL
MEANS
INVENTION

Of all living creatures man was least likely to survive. Without fur or feather,
carapace or scale, he stood naked to the
elements; and without fang or claw to fight his
predators, without the speed to elude them, or
the ability to take to the trees like his cousins
the apes, he was physically at a hopeless disad-
vantage.

What man evolved to deal with his deficiencies was a capacity to invent. He had not only
the ability to perceive; he had imagination. He
did not just improvise to meet a contingency
as the ape did; he planned ahead. At some
point he realized that he could defeat his enemies by outreaching them. It is clever of a baboon to pick up a stone and fling it at an enemy, but it is a big step forward to put that
stone on a stick and use it as a club—a step no
baboon is capable of taking since it is wholly
conceptual. The club is the extension of the
forearm and the fist. The packed punch that
man used against his own kind could serve
against more dangerous animals, he learned, if
the fist were a stone and the arm were extended by a shaft. The sharp-edged flint that he
used to cut open the skins of animals became,
for offensive purposes, a "fist-fang," a crude
dagger. Inserted in the end of a stick it became a spear to be thrust or thrown. The sling
became a flexible, more powerful form of the
cupped hand. And all of these were a long way,
conceptually and in time, from the bow, the
first device in which energy could be stored
and released at will. All these were the first
tools that man's inventiveness had produced
to help him survive in a perilous world.

The Tower of Babel portrayed as an engineering triumph in a fifteenth-century manuscript.

Like man, his fellow creatures had a set of inherited instincts, their built-in experience. The more intelligent might spontaneously improvise (as an ape will devise an implement to reach the banana he can see above him), but apart from the instinctive preservation of their species these creatures had no grasp of the future. Man had foresight, could plan, and, to his great benefit, developed language, the means for passing acquired knowledge from one generation to another. Thomas Carlyle called man, inadequately, a "tool-using animal"; Benjamin Franklin defined man, more properly, as a "tool-making animal." The distinction is important, and if Franklin had added "with foresight" his definition would have been complete.

With nimbleness of brain and hand, the conjunction of gray matter and motor cells, man could plan means not only to outreach or outmaneuver his natural enemies, but to outwit nature itself. He mastered fire and dared to bring it into his dwelling; he learned to plant and cultivate the soil, to domesticate and breed animals; and, in the course of time and his own development, he learned to make simple mechanical devices that greatly improved the efficiency of his labor. By these means he could, as it were, trick nature into helping him.

He did the same when he invented machines. The terms "mechanization" and "machine" actually derive from the Greek *mechanaomai*, "I contrive a deception"—a meaning we still recognize in the word "machinations." Broadly speaking, the simplest of man's first machines were his tools, for a machine is no more than something that increases a man's work output. But it is probably stretching a point to call an ax or hoe a machine, for today the word is commonly understood to mean an apparatus that has at least some moving parts, and combines several principles into one unit that will produce work. Still, the hoe and the ax are just the simplest applications of principles that today govern moving machinery of the most sophisticated design.

From earliest times and the simplest contrivances, every scientific discovery or technological invention has depended and still depends upon the fruitful conjunction of man, method, and moment. The man, of course, is that conceptual creature who, unlike all other creatures on the planet, is capable of observing, memorizing, and juxtaposing images. He can make a mental design, a techno-poetic fantasy, even if the means to produce it are not available. Six hundred years ago Roger Bacon could imagine the power-driven ship, the horseless carriage, the airplane, the miniaturized servomotor, the helicopter, and the bathysphere; and that latter-day Roger Bacon, H. G. Wells, fifty years ahead of space travel, could describe how his men first got to the moon by means of "cavorite," a fictitious, anti-gravity metal.

A man may have the capacity for invention but he will be a mere dreamer unless he has the method. By this process he makes an observation, moves to an hypothesis (no more than a hunch or shrewd guess), experiments to test the validity of the hypothesis, formulates a theory, and ends by making further tests that

produce the "laws" by which anyone else can go on repeating the results. Without this method a man will miss the moment, or that place in time where circumstances combine to make a discovery possible or an invention practicable. Hero of Alexandria invented a kind of steam engine in the first century A.D., but the real development of that machine had to wait for a rapidly industrializing society with abundant needs for the device. Hero had the method but his work came at the wrong moment. Initially men were limited in their work to the force that their own muscle-power could produce, and some jobs were simply too big for human strength to accomplish. But slowly over the millennia, men contrived deceits to make their work easier, to bring the impossible within reach. One device was the inclined plane. Whereas it might be exhausting or impossible to lift vertically a heavy object even a single foot, it was feasible to move it through the same height up a gradient. If a sled with runners was used the job became even easier. And it was easy to observe that the gentler the grade of an inclined plane the farther you had to push your load to move it a given distance—but you did not have to push it as hard as you would on a steep grade.

Another contrivance was the lever. We cannot even hazard a guess as to just when, or how often, or in how many different places our ancestors discovered that by taking a strong branch and placing it on a stone or a log, serving as a fulcrum, they could transport heavy weights. Certainly it happened thousands of years before the third century B.C., when Ar-

chimedes proclaimed, "Give me a fulcrum on which to rest and I will move the earth." He was propounding the Law of the Lever. If the arm beyond the fulcrum is short and the lifting arm is long, a weight can be moved with proportionate ease. A small boy on a seesaw can lift the weight of his father if he sits at the extreme end of his half and the father on the other half sits close to the center. The more uneven the arms are in relation to each other the more mechanical advantage the long one has over the short one. But just as with the inclined plane, the driving force on the long end (the little boy, for instance) has to move a greater distance than the weight at the other end. If the two arms have a proportion of 1 to 5 in length, a man on the long arm will need only one-fifth the strength required to move the weight directly; but in order to lift it one foot he will have to press the long arm down five feet. To lift the world with Saturn as his fulcrum, Archimedes would have had to stand somewhere beyond the Milky Way!

Another deceit early man contrived was the wheel, a discovery quite remarkable because there was nothing rotary in man's experience. Because it required such a jump of imagination, the wheel, in the genealogy of the machine, was a mutation. One can imagine early men moving heavy objects along on tree trunks, shuffling them from one set of revolving trunks to another, as on the roller-conveyors of today, but it took a big step in imagination and technology to advance to the fixed axle, the hub, and the disc wheel.

Another early indication we have of wheeled vehicles is a pictographic entry on the tablets of the Inanna temple of Erech in lower Mesopotamia, the seat of Sumerian civilization, around 3500 B.C. It shows a sled fitted with four solid wheels. A thousand years later the kings of Ur (a Sumerian city) were being buried along with their wheeled hearses. Several royal tombs at two other Sumerian cities, Kish and Susa, also contain evidence of such vehicles. Since the wood has decomposed and the vehicles are no more than imprints in the soil, it is impossible to make out whether the wheels and the axletrees were of a single piece, like a dumbbell, with the axle and wheel rotating together, or whether the axle was fixed and the disc wheel rotated on a hub. Sumerian pictures usually show a hole in the wheel suggesting a hub, and a peg through the axle suggesting a linchpin. There is substantial evidence of wheeled vehicles before 2000 B.C. in China, the Balkans, Sardinia, Spain, Scandinavia, and the British Isles.

How were wheels made? A cross section of a large-diameter tree could have served, but big trees were not common in many places where the wheel has been identified. They were probably made from wood that was pieced together like the three-slat lid of a barrel, which suggests an ability to draw a true circle, and here, in origin at least, was a real challenge to conceptual man. Perhaps he used a length of cord, fixing one end and marking out a circumference with the other, or a forked stick, or even a wishbone as a compass.

Because we are transportation-minded we tend to think in terms of the vertical wheel,

but equally important in the family tree of the machine is the horizontal wheel, which includes the potter's wheel, probably the first unit designed for mass production. In pottery manufacturing the potter's wheel supplies centrifugal force, generated by at least one hundred revolutions per minute to a piece of clay. The spin-energy requires the potter merely to touch the clay in order to change its overall shape. His hand against the lump of material raises it to a tall, slender form or flattens it into a platter. To us such things may seem absurdly simple, but think of the conceptual adventures of ancient invention—the wheel, the axle, and the socket. In them we have the forerunners of those machines that today turn out massive quantities of cheap production goods.

From the wheel emerged the pulley. Some ingenious person, almost certainly somewhere in the Middle East, discovered that the weight-shifting properties of the rigid lever could be reproduced by a rope passing over a roller or wheel. The origin of the pulley is unknown, but the word for pulley still used in modern Arabic is found on a tablet of the fifteenth century B.C. in Syria.

The pulley is a far more sophisticated piece of apparatus than the lever, for it translates mechanical effort into a more versatile form. Imagine the old rope-manipulated elevator, with its weights-and-pulley system that enabled an attendant with a nonchalant pull of the rope to hoist a cage of coal or a cabinful of passengers. He had to pull the rope through a distance many times greater than that traveled by the elevator, but it enabled him with only the strength in his arms to raise a load many times his own weight.

In its simplest form a pulley is a fixed wheel that simply reverses the direction of effort needed to do a job; with such a pulley a man can lift a weight by pulling down on a rope, but it takes as much strength as it would for him to lift the weight without the pulley. He begins to gain mechanical advantage only when he makes his pulley movable and fixes the rope that runs through it to a solid point overhead; then, lifting a weight attached to the pulley itself, he needs to exert only half the strength needed before, although he must pull the rope twice as far. In fact, this ratio expresses the advantage that all simple machines produce: if you will travel a longer distance you will not have to work as hard each step of the way. Used in multiples pulleys can raise proportionately heavier weights. Plutarch tells us that Archimedes could mathematically calculate the number of pulleys necessary to lift a given weight with a given force; he knew how to measure mechanical advantage, which is so important in all weight-lifting devices. Technically, mechanical advantage is expressed by a ratio—the weight to be lifted (the father on the end of that seesaw for example) and the force required to lift it with a given mechanical device. If the little boy weighs twenty pounds and his father two hundred, their arrangement on the seesaw had better yield a mechanical advantage of ten or they will not be able to balance. Archimedes is said to have dragged ashore a fully loaded, three-masted ship during an experiment prior to the Second Punic War

The five simple machines, as classified by the ancient Greeks, have supplied the basis of all machines. The wheel, right, serves as a grindstone, or in a more sophisticated form, as the drive wheel of an early locomotive, below. The screw, shown in the form of a screw press, and also as the humble modern bolt, converts circular effort into a vertical one by means of a spiraling wedge. The lever, whether used to pole a boat, opposite, or to move the heavy mechanism of a tractor, offers man a highly useful alternative: he can reduce the force required to perform a task by applying a smaller force over a greater distance. The wedge, on the right as ancient axheads, or as the metal share of the John Deere plow, penetrates hard substances obliquely, thus reducing the resistance. The pulley, the union of wheel and rope, is actually a lever specialized for lifting weights. It can also be used as a driving belt, as in the motor shown below. The five examples in color are of machines on exhibit at the Smithsonian.

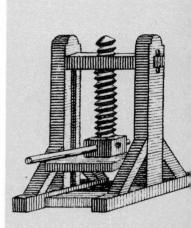

18

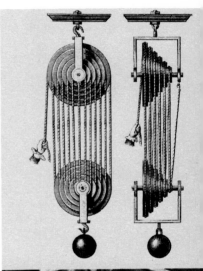

by seizing it with a grapple and hoisting it out of the water by pulleys. Legend also insists that he accomplished the feat single-handed, but he surely would have needed a windlass with an endless screw. The windlass, which coiled the rope on a horizontal drum using vertical hand-levers, and the capstan, a rotating bollard, or post, that was turned by horizontal levers pushed by teams of men, were further developments of mechanical transformation of effort. They are expressed in the formula: driving force times distance moved at driving end equals working force times distance moved at working end. This applies to all simple mechanical devices—the lever, the pulley, the inclined plane, the screw, the wheel and axle. But this of course assumes ideal circumstances that, alas, no machine has ever enjoyed; some energy is always lost to friction between moving parts.

The endless screw translated circular motion into linear motion along the axis of rotation. It was really nothing more than a long inclined plane wrapped around a cylinder or post to make a spiral. One of the screw's functional forms was certainly the water screw (attributed to Archimedes), a long cylinder with a screw fitted inside as closely as a piston. With the lower end of the cylinder immersed in water, the screw, when turned, raised the water.

In the course of time and of various inventions, add teeth to the wheel and a ratchet to the windlass; transform the reduction principle of the pulley into a gear wheel, the lever into a crank, and the haulage rope of the crane into the endless belt of the drive pulleys; and

one has the essential elements which, whatever their refinements and complexities, still form the moving parts of machinery. The Greeks categorized their machinery into the "simple five"—the lever, the wheel and axle, the pulley, the inclined plane, and the screw. The latest model Rolls-Royce purring along a modern highway traces its aristocratic pedigree back to the same humble origins. We still refer to the most elegant limousine in terms of so much "horsepower," a reminder that driving force was for so long animate power and in most of the world still is.

Without these five essential machines work was infinitely harder, if possible at all. The wedge and the lever enabled Egyptian engineers to build in honor of King Cheops the largest of the pyramids. Vast blocks of stone, some weighing fifteen tons, had to be hauled, raised, and set into place—all without the aid of the wheel or pulley. Nor did they use animals to do the arduous work. Cheops' engineers had hordes of peasants, forced to donate their labor as tribute to the king, quarry limestone for the royal tomb, haul the stone up ramps, load it on barges—with the help of levers—float it down the Nile, unload it onto sleds, and drag the tremendous slabs to the site of the pyramid. Since forced labor provided a bottomless supply of manpower the pyramid builders did not concern themselves with increasing the efficiency of their crews. But crews a fraction of the size would have sufficed had they employed the wheel and pulley.

It is stunning to consider the work possible

using just the basic machine forms. One man, aided by mechanical devices known in Roman times, could have moved, all by himself, a family dwelling from a valley to a hilltop. He needed simply the jacks (based on the principle of the screw) to raise it, a strong wheeled cart to place under it, pulleys to haul it, once again the jacks to lower it, and finally a lever to adjust its position on the ground. The moving force was his own muscle, but his ingenuity could multiply the value of that manifold.

The technical term for what drives a machine is "prime mover." In antiquity the only known prime mover was muscle-power, the animate energy (conversion of food-calories) furnished by human beings, oxen, or much later, by horses. Obviously this source of power had its limits. To express muscle-power in an extravagant and barely imaginable example: if a modern transatlantic liner were a galley ship it would take three and a half million slaves pulling on oars to row it from New York to Southampton in five days. Although nature provided and demonstrated enormous sources of power—the sun, water current, wind, thunderstorms, hot springs, hot gases, and natural fuels—man was slow to harness and use any alternative to muscle-power. All he did was devise machines to use it more economically.

From the beginning of the historical record to the sixteenth century, man made remarkable progress in writing, mathematics, astronomy, timekeeping, metallurgy and navigation; in other words, in the exercise and expression of his mental faculties. Still he made comparatively little progress in exploiting the numerous sources of power available to him.

Two exceptions were the harnessing of wind and waterpower. Wind was early recognized as a means of reducing the effort of rowing. By the time of the Egyptian Fifth Dynasty, about 2500 B.C., sailing ships, developed long before to take advantage of the prevailing north wind up the Nile, were large enough to go to sea. But wind remained an auxiliary, and not the principle prime mover at sea, mainly because slaves were cheap and human compassion, as we understand it, was rare.

Another important invention utilizing the power of wind was the windmill, a combination of the sail and the treadmill, presumably of Oriental descent. The idea of the windmill came west through that marketplace of East-West exchange—Persia. Perhaps the Arabs brought the windmill to Europe, or maybe the Crusaders imported it from the Middle East. Perhaps it was independently reinvented in Germany. In any case, from the twelfth to the fifteenth centuries the construction and use of windmills spread all over Europe, especially in Holland, where consistent sea winds made it the archtypa windmill country. One cultural differentiation changed the windmill's form between Persia and Europe: the fixed-pedestal windmill of the Middle East became the tacking and veering turret-windmill of the more navigation-minded West. By the close of the sixteenth century windmills were common enough in Europe for Cervantes to feel confident that no one would wonder what his hero Don Quixote was tilting at.

Our ancestors early recognized the transport value of running water. They saw that logs or rafts could easily be moved by free-flowing currents, but the conversion of those currents into a prime mover required conceptual, not perceptual, thought. It needed imagination relating many factors, and it also needed a mental somersault to see the reverse of a process.

The so-called "Persian wheel" or săqiya that is still used in the Middle East was a familiar device for lifting water. A series of buckets attached to the rim of a vertical wheel scooped up water and at the top of their turn poured it into a sluice. It was powered by animals going around and around in circles, turning a toothed horizontal wheel that meshed with a toothed vertical wheel, that in turn drove the bucket wheel. The mechanism thus depended on the invention of the gear wheel, which has been attributed—probably wrongly—to Archimedes, but which certainly dates to his time (212 B.C.). The săqiya was refined when built-in scoops replaced the pots around the circumference, which brings us near to the paddle wheel of the steamboat. Hindsight makes it simple for us to deduce that if the weight of water could be raised in such a way, the weight of falling water against the paddle wheels could reverse the mechanism and thus power the horizontal wheel. But it was a long time before anyone made that connection.

Later waterpower mills were based on the paddle wheel principle, but, strangely, the earliest watermill of which we know was quite different and was the precursor of the water turbine. It consisted of a horizontal wheel fitted with scoops that were then placed in a strong

A water mill for grinding grain, a Roman invention, used the power of water to drive a vertical paddlewheel. To provide horizontal motion for the upper millstone, H, a cogged wheel, D, is fitted to a trundle, E, with ten upright staves. Grain is fed into the hopper, kk, and when ground emerges through a chute, M, by centrifugal force. By the sixteenth century it could generate up to fifty horsepower.

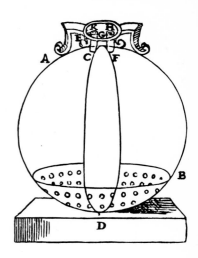

current. A vertical axle connected it to a double millstone above, the upper stone of which moved against the lower, stationary stone so that corn could be ground between them. The whole affair depended on a fast-moving stream, often intensified by a chute. The mill was a low-performance power-mechanism suitable only for domestic, non-commercial corn grinding, and though it is known as the Norse mill, it almost certainly originated in the Near East. It did not provide a new level of energy-production: it merely represented a shift of motive-power from animal muscle to a machine propelled by running water. The Norse mill did, however, inspire some unknown Roman inventor to construct a more efficient mill and make water, at last, an effective prime mover. It is sometimes called the Vitruvian mill because its later variations are described in the works of Marcus Vitruvius Pollio, an official under Emperor Augustus.

There were three subtypes of the vertical wheel—undershot, overshot and breast. The first stood in a stream with the current flowing beneath, pushing the paddles that turned the wheel. It depended on a swift, natural flow without the need for channeling the water. The overshot wheel relied on the full weight of descending water hitting the top of a bladed wheel from a well directed chute. It was a much more efficient machine but required a regulated source such as a dam, sluice, or mill-race. The third (breast) was a compromise, the stream hitting the wheel at axle level and flowing underneath.

Since the technology and performance of water mills were so well established in the first few decades of the Christian era, it is remarkable how slowly waterpower was adopted. Its general acceptance was deferred until late in the Middle Ages, and the heyday of water as a prime mover came just before it was outrivaled by steam (although it would come into its own again with hydroelectricity).

There were, nonetheless, a few spectacular installations, such as the one constructed in 308 A.D. at Barbegal, near Arles, France, which might be described as the earliest power station. Its sixteen overshot waterwheels drove mills that could produce twenty-eight tons of meal in a ten-hour working day, enough to feed a population of eighty thousand. The assemblage was the most ambitious for many centuries.

In the 1680's the Palace of Versailles was built for Louis XIV, and to supply water for its fountains a waterwheel installation was constructed at Marly on the Seine. Its fourteen waterwheels, each forty feet across, drove 221 pumps that raised 870,000 gallons of water every day. The installation pumped water for the exquisite fountains where Louis XIV and his son Louis XV entertained the royalty of Europe. It had cost a fortune to build but its total output was only about eighty horsepower, which today you could find attached to the stern of a rowboat.

After muscle-power, wind power, and waterpower came the transformation wrought when men began to harness the power of steam. There is an irresistible temptation to find in Hero of Alexandria, two thousand years ago,

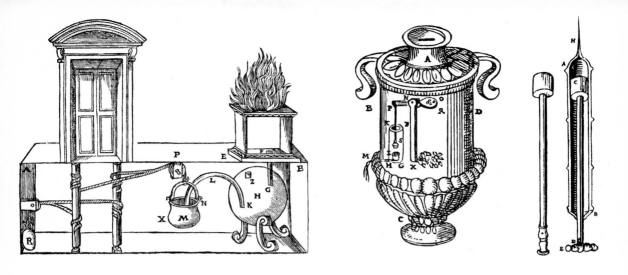

the inventor of the steam turbine and jet propulsion. Hero's "aeolipile" might properly be described as a steam windmill.

His essay *Pneumatica* describes a metal sphere pivoted at the equator on two vertical right-angled tubes that fed steam into a ball from a boiler underneath. At the north and south poles of the sphere were right-angled jets, the top one facing in the opposite direction from the bottom, through which the steam escaped, forcing the sphere to spin. Clearly there was an important idea in Hero's machine, but it never came to anything; the device remained just another of his toys and mechanical juggling tricks.

Altogether Hero is a tantalizing character. We know very little about him; even his dates can be traced no more exactly than to the first century A.D. We do not know whether he was an early Edison who was actually responsible for the many inventions associated with his name or merely a technological encyclopedist. Or perhaps, as his first vending machine and his mechanical puppets suggest, he was essentially an enterprising showman. But from his accounts we know about screw-cutters, about beam presses (which had been known before him and operated on the principle of the lever), and about the combination of the screw and the beam in the screw press, which eliminated the lever action of earlier presses.

Even Hero's toys combined elements of latter machines: the crank, spindle movements with counterweights, and the camshaft, one of the devices that turned the water mill into general-purpose motive-power. In its simplest form the camshaft was a disc that turned off center, so that it could change a rotating motion into a reciprocal or discontinuous one. It could be used to operate treadles, bellows, hammers, or saws. Hero also had cogs, gears, pistons and cylinders, and inlet and delivery valves. Indeed, his writings are a feasibility report on the ideas that would become the power-machines of the nineteenth century.

Why, therefore, if the basic technology was known, did those developments not come two thousand years earlier? First, let us be quite heretical and point out that the Greeks and Romans were not half as enterprising as the classicists would have us believe. The culture that we inherited from the Greeks was synthetic in that it made use of many elements of the cultures with which it had contact, with which it traded, and which it later dominated. The original Greek culture was that of a simple European type—of Odysseus constructing his own marriage bed, and of Penelope the weaver. Like all other Western Iron Age cultures, as distinguished from the Bronze Age, alluvial-plain civilizations, Greece depended on small peasant holdings, mainly on dry hilly ground. The Greek city states relied to a great extent on exports for the acquisition, not of luxuries like the Egyptian and Middle-Eastern importers, but of necessities. When they satisfied those necessities the luxury that the Greeks indulged in was high-thinking; Greek contributions were to politics and to natural science, especially mathematics and astronomy. What differentiated the Greeks from earlier civilizations was a capacity to separate verifiable in-

The crane, at least its nine-teenth-century variety, was a fairly simple machine. To lift a heavy weight, a hand-turned winch, A, moves a trundle, B, which turns gear wheel C and its axle. By a similar gear setup, operating in reverse fashion, the ver-tical axis G is turned, winding the main rope, H, which passes through a pulley and lifts the weight. To shift the raised weight laterally, the crane's essential func-tion, the vertical axis, or gib, cc, is rotated by turning wheel Z. The weight is kept from accidentally falling by a ratchet wheel, Q, and a catch, R, which prevent a reversal of rotation. To keep the main rope from bend-ing it is passed over rollers, pppp, attached to a lever bar, LM. These rollers are held firmly against the rope by the counterweight O, an upward pressure that also insures that the rope will wind evenly around axis G, one coil above the other.

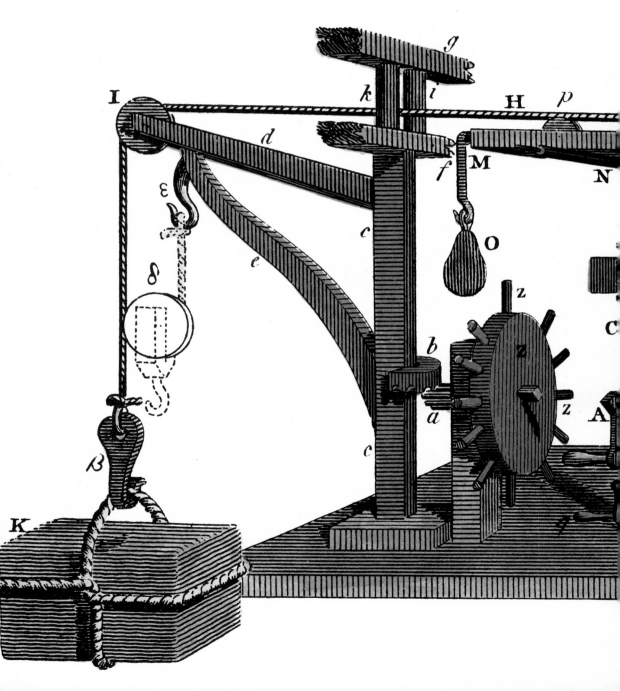

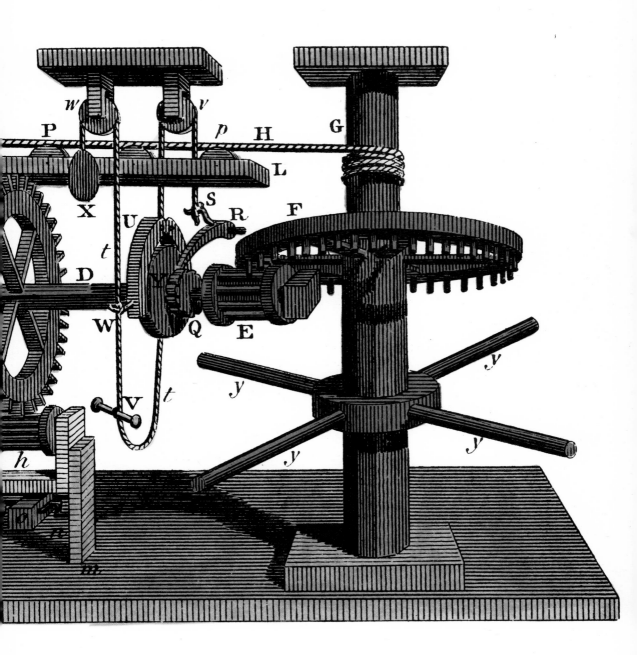

formation from emotional and traditional acceptances. The exercise of pure logic, with geometry as its highest expression, liberated the Greeks from superstition. As philosophers they despised the mechanical arts, and their attitude produced an intellectual aristocracy at the expense of the craftsman. This was abetted by the extension of slavery through wars of conquest. Although much craftwork was still done by free men, the value of their crafts was degraded by the workshop competition of slaves. Workshops were organized for mass production by manual labor, because this offered the simplest way to oversee slave labor. The skills of the craftsman were broken down into separate specialties that could be handled by the semi-skilled.

Just as the twentieth-century worker sees his skills being reproduced and replaced by automation, so in Greece the arts and crafts were being processed, but by muscle-machines—men and women. As a result there was a skills-drain. Instead of exporting manufactured goods, Greece exported craftsmen who could not stand up against competition from the workshops. They immigrated to new colonies, whose products competed with the old, established industries of Greece itself. By the time of Alexander the Great, the foreign adventures that gave him his name and a vast chunk of the ancient world were compulsive. In the fourth century B.C. there was little option for the dispossessed peasants or unemployed workers but to volunteer for foreign service. Thereafter we have Archimedes "of Syracuse," Philo "of Byzantium," and Hero "of Alexandria."

The Greek philosophers could speculate on the nature of the universe or work out the mathematics of mechanical processes, but there was little scientific contact between the men who did the thinking and the men who did the work. Inventions atrophied or, like Hero's, were preserved in books to incite imaginations centuries later. But it should be kept in mind that in a slave-economy there was no pressing need for a new power source such as steam. Indeed, human muscle-labor remained preferable even to animal power, largely because of an ignorance of animal anatomy that even Aristotle did not correct. Since oxen had been used with great advantage over the centuries for ploughing, the ox-harness was unquestioningly transferred to asses, mules, and horses, even though the throat-and-girth harness was quite unsuitable for these animals because of the difference between their body structure and that of the ox. Thus instead of pulling fifteen times as much as a man could, most animals pulled barely four times as much. Because the amount of food consumed by a horse was also four times what a man ate, and because "sense" could be whipped into a slave, human labor was more economical, especially since the Greeks and Romans had no proper shoes for draft animals, whose feet quickly wore out.

Such science as the Romans had was derivative and imitative. Their technology focused on construction, and they perfected principles that enabled them to build with highest competence columns, aqueducts, roads, and

ships. Such engines as they had were military and not too original at that. The long period of Rome's dominance can, in the evolution of the machine, be compared to the age of the dinosaurs in biological evolution; we can be impressed by the colossal remains but will find few surviving progeny in the machine-families of today. Urban planning, civil engineering, architecture, yes. Vitruvian water mills, yes. But there are few mechanical innovations that we would not have had without the Romans.

The trouble is that we have our geography and time scales wrong. Ever since the Renaissance, the debt of the Western World to Greece and Rome has been overemphasized. There is only occasional recognition of the contribution of the Arabs, themselves influenced by the technology of India and China. Only now, through the monumental works of Joseph Needham (*Science and Civilization in China*), are we beginning to put the time-parameters of history in better balance.

Consider and compare the dates of just a few of the Chinese contributions: the triphammer mill with water power—second to first century B.C. (Europe, 1607); the rotary winnowing machine with crank handle—40 B.C. (Europe, very late in the eighteenth century); waterpowered blowing machines for furnaces and forges—second to first century B.C. (Europe, thirteenth century); silk-weaving machinery—before 100 B.C. (Europe, end of the thirteenth century); the spinning top (helicopter)—320 A.D. (Europe, eighteenth century); gunpowder—eighth century A.D. (Europe, thirteenth century); a compass used for navigation—eleventh century (Europe, twelfth century); the knowledge of magnetic declination—1030 (Europe, 1450); papermaking—105 A.D. (Europe, about 1150); movable metal type—1340 (Europe, about 1440).

The growth of Christianity may have modified attitudes toward slavery (although feudal serfdom was not far removed from it), but in terms of questioning the apparent mysteries of nature it hardened man's imaginative processes. When the Roman Empire collapsed—from its own inherent weaknesses as much as from the attacks of the barbarians (who had turned Iron Age technics to better account)—civilization moved northwards to find expression in an age of guilds and craftsmen. But the Mother Church, which replaced the fallen empire, had its own forms of discipline. Inquisitiveness became heresy, and whereas the Greek philosophers had method in their deductive reasoning, the Neoplatonists had intolerance in their dogma.

Yet there were minds that ventured out during the Dark Ages; modern historical research does not confirm the conventional picture of an age of sinister, furtive alchemists in league with the devil. Men like Roger Bacon, Duns Scotus, and William of Ockham were genuine scholars, whose thinking was not locked in by tradition or prejudice. And as slavery receded, other sources of power had to be developed. Horses and mules were properly harnessed during the Middle Ages; water mills and windmills spread across Europe. Far from languishing, machinery began to take on far more sophisticated forms.

THE BONE
AND TISSUE

The three requisites for technological advance—the man, the method, and the proper moment in time—are of little value without the stuff to fashion inventions from: that is, the material. A technoculture can manifest itself only in the materials available. The Eskimos, for example, although an ingenious people and blessed with a remarkable memory, never developed beyond the Neolithic because of their very limited materials. They had no access to ores that might have set them on the track of metallurgy; cold and snow prevented agriculture and made them hunters; they had no wood as they were beyond the tree line, and the lack of other plant life denied them fibers for weaving. Exposed to modern technology, however, Eskimos show immediate technical capabilities, but without these materials they simply were unable to evolve their own technology.

In historical terms we express the working of materials as culture stages—Palaeolithic (Old Stone Age), Neolithic (New Stone Age), Bronze Age, and Iron Age. The designations refer not so much to time as to stages of development; Neolithic is a more advanced stage than Palaeolithic, not just because the people of that period made more efficient weapons or tools, but because they were inventive in other ways as well. Instead of living off hunting and food gathering, Neolithic men turned to tilling, to domesticating animals, and to cultivating plants; instead of using skin or leather pouches they made baskets, a skill that led them to weave plant fibers into cloth to replace pelts as their clothing. They not only cooked their food but made an art of it; they knew how to produce fermented drinks; and instead of living in caves, like animals, they built dwellings of wood and stone. They began to make pottery, finding in fired clay a more plastic, amenable version of stone. What distinguished these people from their predecessors was their experimentation with the materials they found at hand. The man who first imagined, then tried to weave, the first baskets, finally produced them and taught others to do the same. He made a technological discovery that helped to lift his people into a new stage of development.

Where nature leaves something conveniently handy—like a flintstone or a piece of alluvial native copper—the observant man will turn it to his specialized uses. Finding it useful, he will work to find more when the immediate supply gives out. He will grow ever more ingenious. Having begun with antlers or limbbones as a tool, in a moment of discovery he will heat rocks and douse them with cold water to split them, and thus make for himself implements of stone. He will learn to sluice the sediments of streams for ore fragments. He will quarry outcrops until they are flattened, and then mine what he wants by driving in tunnels or sinking vertical shafts.

Step by step, all this is possible to perceptual man. But he becomes really clever when he thinks conceptually, when he puts dissociated observations together. Metallurgy was one of the first pursuits man followed by conceptualizing, rather than simply perceiving. Metallurgy proper began when some imaginative man,

or men, realized that by smelting, heating, and casting they could give metal new and controlled forms far beyond what chipping, splitting, cutting, and grinding had ever produced. This realization came over six thousand years ago somewhere in the Near East, and it depended upon someone making a remarkable association between certain stones and the metals inherent in them.

Silver was probably the first metal to be extracted in any quantity from its source, a mineral called galena, which also holds lead. Refined silver, pure lead, and pigs (crude lead castings) were in commercial production by the end of the third millenium B.C. Gold—that glittering promise that has haunted so many generations—came next, obtained with much less difficulty, since it is found in its natural state. In time these metals taught men the principles of smelting and refining, and their cultures advanced significantly whenever they applied these principles to finding more useful metals.

Except for ornamentation, copper is far more useful than gold or silver. Ancient Egyptians, as early as 5000 B.C., used malachite (a powdered form of a basic carbonate of copper) as a green eye shadow. About the time Menes founded the first Egyptian dynasty in 3200 B.C., someone discovered that malachite was fusible; that is, it would melt over heat and could be smelted into a hard copper that made good weapons. These weapons, in turn, made Menes master of upper and lower Egypt. The ancient Egyptian method of producing copper was to mix broken malachite with charcoal, either in a heap on the ground or in a shallow pit, where the wind could fan the fire. (An excellent example of this system can be found at King Solomon's Mines in the Negev Desert of Israel, where a gulley provides a prevailing draft and slag heaps still testify to the ancient practice.) It was also early discovered how to anneal (heat and cool) native copper to remove the brittleness that hammering produced.

Although copper altered the societies that discovered it, it had limitations just as stone did. Copper is a poor metal for casting because it contracts on cooling and becomes porous. But tin mixed with copper in the molten state checks the copper's absorption of oxygen and other gases and produces the alloy called bronze. Its early history is obscure; we know simply that it was an Asiatic discovery made at least as early as 3500 B.C. Probably bronze was discovered accidentally through the smelting of mixed ores containing both copper and tin. It proved, in any case, a far more serviceable metal than copper, and even gave its name to an epoch.

But bronze produced small technological advances compared to what iron did after it. The iron ore used in predynastic times—around 3000 B.C.—was hematite, a mineral that can be fashioned into beads, amulets, and other ornaments, and into such compounds as ochres, siennas, and umbers, which were used as pigments and cosmetics. (It is a sobering thought that machine-technology may have been founded on women's vanity!) But this was simply the available iron immediately apparent in a fairly pure state in meteoric rock, and it was worked with the methods applied to stone and precious stone. No culture reached the Iron Age until it learned to extract iron from the ores where it existed.

The Iron Age began in the Near East sometime around 1200 B.C., although iron farm tools had been in use in China for several centuries. Its rather late arrival in the West is strange because a copper smelter used a furnace quite capable of extracting iron oxides, and copper smelting had been known for about three thousand years. A probable explanation is that smelting iron ore in a way familiar for obtaining copper produced nothing but a clump of fused stone, riddled with holes and looking singularly unmetallic; the iron still lay concealed. Only by heating and hammering in endless succession could the slag be removed and the metal particles battered into a lump of wrought iron, and only a broad leap in the copper or bronze smelter's imagination could have inspired him to try a process so far removed from his ordinary practices. Then, even when someone had finally wrought it, the iron obtained was still no better than the copper or bronze that he could produce so much more easily, and with considerably less fuel. Thus as long as the copper supplies lasted there was no urgent reason for working to obtain iron. At some point, however, men discovered that if they repeatedly hammered and heated the wrought iron (unwittingly introducing carbon by contact with the charcoal they used as fuel), and then plunged it into cold water, they got an iron with a hardness superior to that of bronze. Only when this carbonized iron be-

came available did the Iron Age proper commence. Actually, it is the introduction of carbon from the fuel into iron that produces steel, and early iron workers developed a system of hammering, heating, and slow cooling that converted the surface of an iron object into steel. The identification of the element carbon, and the recognition of the part it played in steelmaking would not take place until the late eighteenth century, but usable iron and steel were produced for a very long time, however, without any understanding of their chemical composition.

History was wrought with iron. Instead of being a rare metal that had to be imported at great cost from distant mines, it was one of the most common elements to be found in the earth's surface. Once the proper means of producing it had been mastered, it made a far tougher material for weapons and machinery than any metal that preceded it. It helped create one of history's first classes of technical specialists—the smith.

Ironworking first flourished under the Hittite kings, who ruled in Asia Minor from 1600 to 1200 B.C. The Chalybes, a people who were subjects of the Hittites, made a specialty of ironworking, and it was they who first discovered how to convert the surface of wrought iron into steel. They lived and worked mainly in the Armenian mountains, and when invading Thracians and Phrygians ended the rule of the Hittite kings, the ironsmiths dispersed throughout the Middle East, carrying their trade with them like technical colonists.

Spreading out slowly in waves from the

Middle East, ironworking overtook the Neolithic peoples of Europe, leaping the hurdles of previous cultural evolution. It gave them the ax to cut down the forest and the plow to furrow heavy loams. It shod their horses, riveted their armor, edged their swords, and forced less technically enterprising civilizations to make way for them. It developed their crafts and, because iron lent itself to applications that stone, wood, and even bronze had never conceded, it made the European "barbarians" far more mechanical-minded than the Greeks or the Romans. Wrought iron, cast iron, and steel gave them durable wheels, cogs and pulleys, ratchets, and cams. It gave them better cutting edges, like the saw and—pause and consider its implications—the file. They could now cut metal screws and construct lathes, neither of which could have been done as well with copper or bronze.

Although cast iron was used extensively in China as early as the sixth century B.C., in Europe iron was the metal of the smith, not the foundryman, until the fifteenth century A.D. At about that time Europeans began to smelt the ore in a tall blast furnace, where the reduced iron remained in close contact with the carbon of the fuel, thus becoming further carbonized and eventually melting so that it could be separated from the slag. Then the resulting cast iron was converted into wrought iron by further refining.

The different natures of wrought iron, cast iron, and steel, not understood until Réaumur's analysis at the end of the eighteenth century, lay in what proportion of carbon had been introduced into the iron from the charcoal of the furnace. But whatever the proportion was, charcoal provided the only known fuel that made a fire hot enough to smelt iron. Since charcoal is produced by partially burning wood, the restraint on the general manufacture of iron was the availability of timber. Deforestation of vast areas (the forests of southern England became the bald sheep-runs of the South Downs) finally crippled iron production. It did not revive until early in the eighteenth century when Abraham Darby of Coalbrookdale in Shropshire, England, discovered that by coking (precooking) coal, the fossil-fuel from the carboniferous forests of millions of years ago, he could produce a substitute for charcoal. His discovery turned the gracious midlands into the Black Country, and prepared the way for that rapid proliferation of machines called the Industrial Revolution.

Mining and metalworking are entwined as cause and effect in the long history of the machine. Numerous pumps were devised to raise water from mines and these, as we shall see, eventually led to the steam engine and the locomotive. Waterpower and water mills found early applications in powering huge bellows and mechanical hammers used in metalworking. Moreover, mechanized metalworking launched capitalism. During the second half of the fourteenth century, after the Black Death and the Hundred Years' War, a shortage of labor caused a drastic decline in both mining and metal production. Without enough skilled craftsmen to operate individual forges it was necessary for separate works to be consolidat-

ed into bigger units, and smelting and forging had to be mechanized. The heavy capital expenditure this required was possible only with the help of the bankers, and their help began the system of massive capital investment in expanding industry.

There were certainly materials other than iron that were basic to technological progress. Glass was one. It goes back a long way, and not surprisingly, since a hot enough wood fire on sand will produce silica fused with soda ash, the liquid ingredients that, when hardened, form glass. Therefore, any culture that could produce the pottery kiln and the ore furnace could produce glass. The craft of glassmaking (for trinkets, stained-glass windows, mirrors) has a quaint and interesting history, but in the pedigree of the machine and the ancestry of modern advances in technology its contributions were strangely dilatory. The first glass instrument to receive the attention of the scientific researcher was the thermometer. Early in the seventeenth century Santorio Sanctorius of Padua improved on Galileo's version of the heat-measuring instrument and produced the first clinical thermometer. Its success was a boon to the glassblowers of Florence. The art of glassmaking, however, was still in its infancy as late as the last part of the seventeenth century, when Anton van Leeuwenhoek produced that all-important contribution to man's understanding of nature, the microscope.

Among the most important materials in the history of the machine is a non-material—the vacuum. One might say it demonstrated the importance of being nothing. In 1654 Otto von Guericke of Magdeburg conducted his famous demonstration of the power of non-matter before the Imperial Diet of Ratisbon. He arranged for two carefully matched hollow bronze hemispheres to be held fast by nothing more than a vacuum, created by the first use of an air pump, which he had devised for the occasion. Eight horses harnessed to each hemisphere were unable to drag them apart, and only when a valve was opened to let the air in again could they be separated. Robert Hooke and Robert Boyle of England, Christian Huygens of Holland, and Denis Papin of France all improved on the methods of making non-matter, and by the eighteenth century air pumps were being produced commercially.

In the inventory of materials for machinery and industry, a late arrival but one of enormous significance was what is broadly classified as "plastics." In 1736 the French Académie des Sciences was introduced to the milky sap of a Brazilian tree, brought back by a scientific expedition that had already used this "caoutchouc" (pure natural rubber) to waterproof garments and shoes. The academy had begun the systematic study of products—in the manner of the best modern applied science—and the *caoutchouc* was submitted to a thorough investigation as to: its solubility in water, alcohol, or ether; its reactions to acid, alkali, and other active agents; its behavior when heated or chilled. The academicians knew its properties, but neither they nor the enterprising Scotsman, Charles Macintosh, who used rubber to manufacture raincoats, could overcome its deficiencies. Rubber is un-

stable in its natural qualities and so tends to become brittle in winter and sticky in summer. The problem was solved in 1839 by an American, Charles Goodyear, who began his researches from debtors' prison. He finally discovered that rubber, when heated with sulfur, produced satisfactory results. The addition of 8 to 10 per cent sulfur produced a soft flexible product, while 30 to 40 per cent produced a hard, brittle material that is called "vulcanite." And so was born the first modern plastic. (The adjective is necessary because "plastics" such as shellac, mastic, bitumen, myrrh, and casein were used by ancient civilizations in the Middle and Far East.) Vulcanite was not a true synthetic; it was a modified natural product. The synthetics were to come from the organic chemists. To qualify as a plastic a synthetic material must, at some stage in its history, possess plasticity, that is, the capacity to flow and take a desired shape, even though the end result may be extremely hard and unyielding. The foundations of the present synthetic plastics industry were truly laid in 1907 when Dr. Leo H. Baekeland produced the first phenoformaldehyde in the presence of an acid catalyst, forming a man-made resin.

Synthetic materials to match specific needs, confidently achieved by the organic chemists, challenged the metallurgists to make unmanageable metals manageable. Electrolysis had already transformed aluminum from an intractable laboratory curiosity into a cheap, universal, light metal. Magnesium, lighter still, had been mass-extracted from sea water, but high temperatures, high speeds, and the new require-

ments of atomic energy and electronics called for the handling of unfamiliar metals such as uranium, beryllium, zirconium, titanium, germanium, indium, tantalum, niobium, and molybdenum. Inside-out smelting, which uses ultrashort waves to agitate molecules and generate heat from the inside of a metal, made still rarer refinements possible. Powdered metallurgy, which involved compressing rather than melting, made possible combinations that could not be achieved by molten alloys. Ceramic metals, or metallic ceramics, a long way from the potter's clay, exploited oxides, borides, carbides, and nitrides to make materials that were light, strong, corrosion-resistant, and able to endure high temperatures. Combinations of plastics with metals or glass (such as Fiberglas) opened up even wider possibilities.

This development of "tailor-made molecules," or, in the language of the chemist, "long-chain polymers," was one of the most important points of departure in the evolution of technology. To be able to prescribe a material for a specific purpose and give it predetermined qualities meant that invention was taking on a new dimension. It was no longer a case of "What can we do with the materials we have?" It was now possible to say, "What do we want to achieve? We will make the substances to suit our ends." Suddenly man did not have to limit his technology only to the materials at hand. But it had required those materials first to bring modern Western man to the advanced science of synthetics, while far to the north the Eskimo remained frozen in a stone age of development.

THE CLIMATE
OF INVENTION

In a careless fashion we usually think of the Industrial Revolution in terms of the factory system, the steam engine, and the locomotive, and date it from James Watt's steam engine of 1765. On each count our impression is wrong. The factory system existed in ancient Greece and Rome. England had woolen factories before 1550. Conversely, home manufacture continued long after the steam engine had been introduced. If we want to date the Industrial Revolution by the evolution of machines, we can find its germs as far back as the Black Death in the fourteenth century, when a shortage of labor encouraged the development of machines. In fact the Middle Ages and Renaissance steadily developed the ideas, the technology, and the social conditions that made the Industrial Revolution possible. Its emergence was not a sudden overthrow of conventional technology but a natural outgrowth of the interests and attitudes that preceded it.

Particularly can we find its roots in the Renaissance, which was so much more than just a cultural explosion. The Renaissance, it might be said, was the Age of the Eye, and the artist shared it with the scientist, the scientist with the practical man. In the history of technology the Renaissance is generally remembered for the advent of gunpowder and the printing press, but extraordinarily complex machinery also came into being—at least on paper.

Leonardo da Vinci (1452-1519), that supreme artist and inventor, secretly diagramed in his now famous notebooks a wealth of machinery of such diversity that it suggests a fer-

ment of inventiveness surrounding him, and that, apart from his own extraordinary contributions, he was perhaps making an inventory of the mechanical devices of his time. He foresaw the flying machine, the parachute, the military tank, the paddle-wheel boat, spinning machinery, the turret windmill, roller bearings, the power-driven hammer, a die-press for coinage, screws, and screw-cutting. He suppressed his idea of a submarine "on account of the evil nature of man, who would practice assassination at the bottom of the sea."

One of his devices was a spring-driven clock, an invention that helped push the evolution of the machine in the direction of automation. The ancients had measured time by their calendar, employing sundials, water clocks, and hourglasses. More than a century before Leonardo's design, the workings of a mercury clock were described in a book compiled for King Alfonso X of Spain. The clock operated by a weight that hung from a cord wound around a drum. As the weight fell, very slowly, an annular container of mercury, divided by perforated partitions, controlled the drum's rotation speed. As the drum turned the mercury rose, until it counterbalanced the driving weight. The rate of revolution—communicated to a revolving dial by teeth on the rim of the dial—depended on the viscosity of the mercury and the size of the holes it passed through.

After the mercury clock came the pendulum. One Sunday in 1581 in the cathedral of Pisa, a seventeen-year-old boy named Galileo watched an overhead lamp swing back and forth in a long arc. He timed its swing by his pulse and to his excitement discovered that on a wide arc the lamp swung quickly, and as its arc grew smaller the speed of the swing decreased. Each complete swing, no matter how wide, took the same length of time. Later experiments proved to his satisfaction that for a given length of pendulum the period of oscillation was constant and independent of amplitude. The Dutch mathematician Christian Huygens perfected the use of this observation in the escapement of a clock that served as the acme of accuracy for centuries, or until radio developed to the point where wave lengths had to be allocated to different stations.

To actually make a mechanical clock required precise workmanship, and with increased miniaturization came refinements in gears, escapements, cogs, hands, striking bells, pendulums, and springs. The engineering of timepieces had implications far beyond the mantlepiece or pocket-watch. In a letter to Friedrich Engels in 1863 Karl Marx observed that "the clock is the first automatic machine applied to practical purposes; the whole theory of production and regular motion was developed through it." Lewis Mumford, that great interpreter of technical history, adds the following: "The clock, in fact, is the paragon of automatons: almost all that we can achieve and all that we can expect in automatons was first worked out in the clock. In the progress from the great cathedral clocks of the sixteenth century to the tiny self-winding wrist watch with its calendar and alarm, one finds, too, the earliest example of the process of miniaturization, over which electronic technology currently, and with reason, is so proud. The automation of time, in the clock, is the pattern of all larger systems of automation."

Other factors generally omitted in the careless dating of the Industrial Revolution are social. One was the Commercial Revolution in Britain, which saw the emergence of the merchant companies during the seventeenth and eighteenth centuries, and with them the merchant bankers who could dictate terms to the entrenched guilds and crafts. They forced what might be called the compulsory amalgamation of skills, a kind of diversification of guild monopolies and of "plant unionism" according to crafts. They became the financiers of what modern terminology would define as quality control and development research labs. They set up schools for overseers and the instruction of mine analysts of metals and ores. The role of commercial industry was extended to the financing of mining improvements and the equipping of enterprises, which has been mentioned as the foundation of modern capitalism. With the advance of this new class of merchant capitalists, the last remains of the feudal system slowly disappeared and a new aristocracy of wealth emerged. This in turn brought about, in the seventeenth and eighteenth centuries, the Agricultural Revolution.

By a cynical appropriation of common land, the landed gentry deprived the country freemen of their traditional rights of common grazing; they threw up fences around fields that had fed village livestock for hundreds of years, locking out the freemen and their cattle, and thus denying them the essentials of their livelihood. This move accelerated the migration of farmers into cities. The commoners of the parklands and the verderers of the forest lands became "the landless proletariat," drifting into the towns as factory workers, while the enclosed lands became available for crop rotation and managed animal and plant husbandry, which meant improved and profitable (for the landed gentry) agriculture. With it came bio-aesthetic planning, deliberate tree planting, and the introduction of new species, which today fools people looking at places such as Windsor Great Park or Blenheim into thinking that this is "nature" at its best.

It was the geographical accident of having coal and iron together—both for the making of workable iron and steel and for fuel—that gave Britain a flying start in the Industrial Revolution, which is one of those facts of history we in the West often overlook. With our sometimes myopic view of history we tend to think that some innate superiority in technological intelligence was vested in Western Man. It would be more realistic to recognize that accessible coal and iron determined the nature of the First Industrial Revolution. As the World Power Conference keeps on reminding us, over 90 per cent of the accessible coal and over 80 per cent of the other essential fossil-fuels, oils, and natural gas lie north of latitude 20 degrees north. Countries without such evident resources could not develop as did Britain, the countries of northern Europe, the United States, and Russia, countries we now call "advanced" because they are the heirs of the prosperity of the Industrial Revolution.

The intricately coordinated mechanism of a clock is one of the masterworks of machine technology. The one opposite was built by clockmaker Eli Terry around 1800. The first mechanical clocks, driven by falling weights, were invented in the thirteenth century and proved to be a landmark in man's history. As a self-regulating mechanism, the clock became the model for many future machines. It gave man a new concept of time. Instead of merely marking the succession of events, time—clock time—became an independent reality, something that could serve as a standard for regulating human activities. The nineteenth-century factory, such as the Chicago metal-working shop, below, with its tasks synchronized by fixed intervals of time, would have been impractical without the clock's discipline.

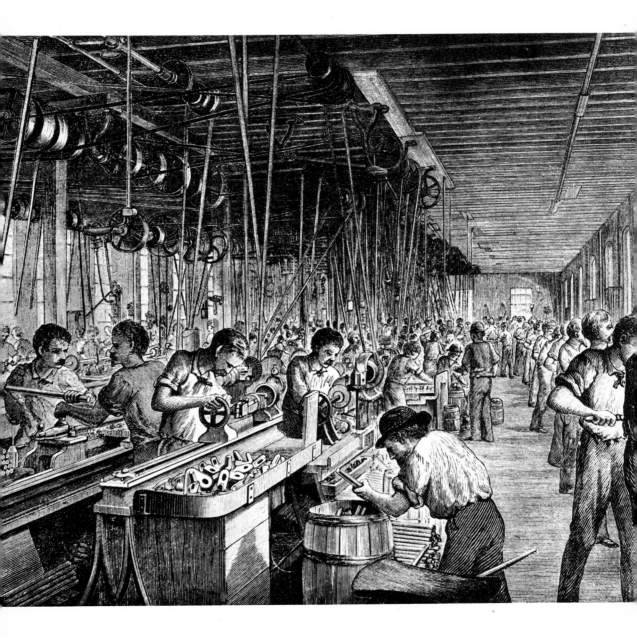

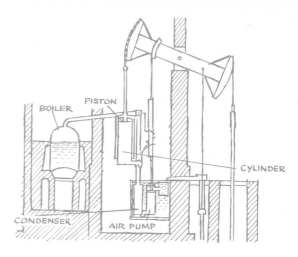

Watt's steam engine, right, in its early form, was used to pump water. When the piston is at the top of its stroke, steam from a boiler rushes into the cylinder. Then a valve between the cylinder and a separate condenser—Watt's chief innovation—is opened. The steam rushes into the water-cooled chamber and condenses, creating a vacuum. Atmospheric pressure drives the piston down. Later it became an all-purpose engine.

BOILER PISTON

CYLINDER

CONDENSER AIR PUMP

The social implications of industrial machinery were greater than almost any of their inventors realized. Of the many machines of the Industrial Revolution which substituted mechanical effort for human drudgery, surely one of the most important was Eli Whitney's cotton gin. Few devices of any period have had such a dramatic impact on history. In 1793, while he was studying law in Savannah, Georgia, Whitney invented a simple and inexpensive apparatus that would remove the tough green seeds from the fibers of cotton. Until then it had been a nearly worthless crop, since to clean a single pound by hand took one man an entire day. Whitney's gin, operated by one man, could clean as much as fifty pounds a day, and because of it cotton suddenly became a cash crop. Production soared from about one hundred thousand bales per year in 1801 to more than five million bales by 1859.

The repercussions of Whitney's machine in human terms were something else again. Negro slavery, which had been slowly dying in the South since the Revolutionary War, quite rapidly became profitable for the planters. Whitney's little "laborsaving device" did as much as anything to encourage the entrenchment of a massive system of slave labor that only a long and bloody war would destroy. It would also leave on the human spirit and human society scars that are still apparent.

But increased cotton production in America also had, understandably, a profound and immediate impact on the European textile industry, which was also being revolutionized by new machinery that had been introduced at

about the time Eli Whitney was born. And already, well before writers such as William Blake warned against the evils of "dark Satanic mills," or factory workers began to portray themselves as "wage-slaves," there was stout, even violent resistance to the advance of mechanization. In England angry workers had invaded James Hargreaves' home and destroyed his famous spinning jennies (invented in 1764), which could spin eight to ten threads at one time; they set about systematically wrecking Richard Arkwright's water frame for carding, roving, and spinning cotton. According to legend one Ned Ludd, a weak-minded boy from Leicester, demolished some stocking frames around 1780, and thenceforth those who took up machine sabotage in industrial England were known as "luddites." In Scotland handloom and power-loom weavers engaged in pitched battles; in France J. M. Jacquard's ingenious brocade silk looms, with their punched card system for regulating designs, brought on riots from which Jacquard barely escaped with his life. Barthélemy Thimonnier's sewing machines caused violent upheavals among tailors in Paris; a mob of them destroyed his shop. But the machine that caused the most serious "ludditism" was the gig mill, a device that raised the nap, or surface, of woolen cloth. In manual practice the cloth was sprinkled with water and rubbed with teasels, the heads of prickly plants. Leonardo da Vinci had designed the original gig mill, a machine driven by a winch turned by a horse. The cloth, its ends sewn together to make a belt, traveled around two rollers under an adjustable beam

Overleaf: James Watt in 1792,
when the Scottish inventor
was fifty-six and British
industry was "steam-mill mad."
Also overleaf: his speed
governor, which paved
the way to modern automation.
Two iron balls revolved
when a vertical spindle
was turned by the steam
engine. As the engine speed
increased, the balls swung
outward, operating connecting
rods that shut a steam
valve to reduce engine speed.

covered with teasel heads. Five lengths of cloth could be raised simultaneously on the same machine. In England the gig mills were in use in the early seventeenth century, and, although banned by Act of Parliament in 1551, their use appears to have continued. But in 1812 the widespread success of the machine aroused violent reactions from clothworkers fighting for the right to keep their jobs scratching woolen fabrics with the heads of thistles.

Still, the advance of industrial mechanization continued, especially in the cotton industry, where machines of astonishing shapes and sizes emerged to do the work of many men. But as important as textile machinery is to the story of the Industrial Revolution, it has to take second place to the steam engine, which represents one of the great turning points in the history of the machine and of mankind. With that invention we can mark the end of the past and the beginning of the present.

In the latter part of the seventeenth century a French Huguenot, Denis Papin, working with Christian Huygens in Holland, and Robert Boyle in England, made the first pressure cooker, which compressed superheated steam in a closed vessel. Papin fitted to the vessel a safety valve with a weight attached. When the pressure in the pot became great enough to equal the force of the weight, it forced the safety valve open and released some of the pressure. His valve was an important link in the lineage of the machine, being one of the first automatic control devices. Papin extended his use of steam to the design of a steam engine, with which he intended to drive a ship against the wind, but it was inefficient, depending more on atmospheric pressure than on the power of expanding steam. To operate it a workman had to push a fire box under a boiler which produced steam, and then haul it out to allow condensation. Papin's chief legacies to the evolution of the machine were the piston and cylinder.

His engine was stillborn, but the idea of a steam engine was freshly conceived later by a gifted English inventor named Thomas Savery, who in 1698 patented "an engine to raise water by fire." To pump water out of deep-shafted mines, Savery had created a partial vacuum by raising steam through pipes and sluicing the outside of the boiler with cold water to produce condensation. But the Savery engine was capable of lifting water to heights of no more than twenty feet; thus its possibilities for mining seemed limited.

In 1712 Thomas Newcomen, an English ironmonger and Baptist preacher, modified Savery's design with a pump that sprayed cold water into a steam-filled cylinder to create a vacuum, making atmospheric pressure force the piston down. Newcomen's machine also featured a huge, overhead, horizontal "rocking beam" that was tipped, or "rocked" up and down by the piston. His were the first steam engines to enjoy a real commercial success. The English coal mining companies put them to immediate use. The machines consumed fantastic amounts of coal for the power they produced, but for sixty years there would be nothing new to compete with the Newcomen engine. Then the Watt engine appeared.

¾ diam

1.2.7.

3/10 Jun

2.1/4

10 7/8

3/8 Jun

1 1/8

6. × 7. 1.

Inch diam

4. × 4.

½ inch Jun.

12 Inches

1/2

1/2

21 Inches   Turn'd the legs — 6 on each side

2 square

2 feet

The Socket to be made
as thin & light as can be.
say ¾ Inch thick.

Globe 8 diam Cast iron

James Watt, of Greenock, Scotland, did not, as legend would have it, discover the steam engine by watching the lid of his mother's tea kettle. He was a "philosophical instrument maker," what we would now call a "laboratory mechanic" at the University of Glasgow, and one day he received for repairs a model of the Newcomen engine that was used for class demonstrations. Watt realized how inefficient the engine was, and during a chat with Joseph Black, a professor of chemistry who had discovered carbon dioxide, he mentioned his own calculations—that a small quantity of steam could heat a quantity of water six times its own weight to 212 degrees F. Black replied by explaining his theory of latent heat, which until then he had mentioned only to his students. Its practical significance dawned on Watt later, as he was walking across Glasgow Green. "I had not walked farther than the Golf house," he wrote, "when the whole thing was arranged in my mind; the waste of heat could be avoided by keeping the boiler at steam heat and condensing the steam in a separate cylinder." Watt had built a new model within days. Joseph Black was so impressed by it that he loaned him twelve hundred pounds to continue working, an investment that permitted Watt to develop the condensing steam engine.

The machine's completion, however, required more financial help than Black had provided. It came by a roundabout path from a Birmingham toymaker ("toy" in those days meant fine ornaments, like shoe and knee-breech buckles) named Matthew Boulton. Boulton had recently built a new factory that was to be powered by a waterwheel, but during the first summer of its operation there was a drought. Since he had just got a profitable contract to mint coins, the lack of power would be a serious financial blow to him. Boulton had an idea; he would use a pump to raise water from the tailrace back to the millpond, and so keep the scare commodity in cycle. He also had ideas of his own about improving Savery's engine. As a founding member of the Lunar Society of Birmingham he wrote for advice to one of its most noted corresponding members, Benjamin Franklin, then in London. Franklin, unfortunately, was too busy with the Stamp Act to assist him. But Franklin had already introduced Boulton to William Small, a Scotsman who taught natural philosophy at Williamsburg. (Thomas Jefferson, one of Small's students, remembered when writing his autobiography that "Small probably fixed the destinies of my life.")

Approached by Boulton for advice on the mill-pump at his toy factory, Small remembered James Watt and brought the two men together. Watt's steam engine might not have materialized but for that eventful partnership. Boulton not only supplied Watt with a regular salary and money to keep on with his work, but also provided his brilliant but easily discouraged partner constant encouragement. Watt was able to apply his understanding of heat to the steam-driven pump, which required only one quarter the fuel that Newcomen's engine needed. He also realized that if a rotary motion was created from the up-and-down motion of the piston and overhead beam,

it would provide an additional source of energy at the other end of the pumping motion. At first he incorporated the flywheel (known since the twelfth century), which is a wheel of large diameter and heavy rim connected to a crank and crankshaft. But the device that came into general use to operate the flywheel was his "sun and planet gear." This was a sophisticated reversal of the circular motion by which the waterwheel powered a bellows. The up-and-down motion of the rod and beam moved the small wheel around the other wheel, which in turn moved the flywheel. Now, along with pumping, this machine could drive wheels and belts, enabling them to perform varied mechanical tasks.

One day William Murdock, a gangling young man from Ayrshire, applied to Boulton for a job in his engine factory. He was so nervous at the interview that he dropped his top hat, and when Boulton picked it up he discovered it was made of wood. The applicant, Boulton learned, had made it on a lathe he had designed and built himself. He got the job. Presently he went to Cornwall to work as the engine-builder for the Boulton-Watt interests.

Murdock was an inventive genius. For one thing, he wanted to put the steam engine on wheels, so he built a model locomotive that provided new mobility to the Boulton-Watt engine. He had difficulties in testing it indoors, so he took to "exercising" it on the roads at night. Legend has it that on one of those furtive night trials the model, breathing fire and smoke, ran out of control and raced after the vicar of the local parish, supplying him his ser-

mon for the following Sunday, on which he vividly delineated "the beast of the Revelation" that had appeared as a warning to his sinful community. Murdock was prepared to abandon his job to go to London and promote his engine, but Matthew Boulton, like an irate father chasing an eloping bride, intercepted him and sent him back to Cornwall, where his experiments led to what eventually became the gas industry.

The first steam-powered creation that can be justly termed a locomotive was built by a Cornish wrestler and mining engineer named Richard Trevithick. In 1801 he constructed an iron coach, the *Puffing Devil*, and drove the first passengers on wheels. It broke down. His second steam carriage set off on the road to London, but its engine was completely worn out upon its arrival there. Trevithick thus concluded that the locomotive was not suitable for the open road. As an alternative he decided to put it on rails.

In 1804 he conducted a demonstration run of the world's first true locomotive. His single-cylinder steam locomotive built for the Penydarin Iron Works in Wales pulled 10 tons of iron and 70 passengers in 5 wagons at a speed of 5 miles per hour along a 10-mile tramway. Later he displayed an improved model on a circular track in London. It was known as the *Steam Circus*, but it proved a financial fiasco. Afterwards he managed to get backing for a scheme to cut a tunnel under the Thames. It was three feet wide by five feet high and had progressed a thousand feet before it flooded. Then Trevithick went to South America,

where he became known as the man whose pumps had salvaged the silver mines of Peru. Shortly he became a man of property there, but when Simon Bolivar came along to liberate the country from colonialist rule, men of property were not popular. Barely escaping with his life, Trevithick tried various projects elsewhere in South America and finally found himself penniless in Panama, where a young engineer, taking pity on the legendary inventor, gave him his fare home. The Good Samaritan was the son of George Stephenson, and the money was a first dividend from the Stockton-and-Darlington Railway that had succeeded exactly where Trevithick had failed.

Meanwhile, William Murdock had developed gas from carbonized coal as a commercial possibility. In Birmingham he floodlit the Boulton-Watt factory with flaming gas jets to celebrate the Peace of Amiens. Thus Sir Walter Scott appropriately called him "the man who lit London with smoke."

Steam was to provide the power for the tireless and exacting machines of the Machine Age, and gas was to light the factories where they operated. By the nineteenth century machines had so invaded human society—at least in northern Europe—that the great English writer Samuel Butler wrote a book (*Erewhon*, or "nowhere" upon juxtaposition) that depicted a bleak utopia in which the machine became the master of man. He wrote: "Even now the machines will only serve on condition of being served and that too upon their own terms; the moment their terms are not complied with, they jib and either smash both themselves and all whom they can reach, or turn churlish and refuse to work at all. How many men at this hour are living in a state of bondage to the machines? How many spend their whole lives, from the cradle to the grave in tending them by night and day? Is it not plain that the machines are gaining ground upon us, when we consider the increasing number of those who are bound down to them as slaves, and of those who devote their whole souls to the advancement of the mechanical kingdom?"

In Samuel Butler's time factories and locomotives ran by means of wheels, pulleys, belt-driven shafts, cranks, cams, cogs, and ratchets, essentially the same components that drove any gentleman's pocket watch; and, indeed, the highest compliment one could pay to any system was that it ran "like clockwork." The engineers who devised and improved upon the systems of Butler's era traced their heritage directly to Isaac Newton. Like Newton, they perceived the universe as a reliable, predictable mechanism. Newton's and theirs were ages of immense self-confidence, of cause and effect, with little room for uncertainty. You pulled a lever, the gears meshed, and the machine proceeded to do its work. But the engineers assumed that a human arm must pull that lever. The idea of complete automation had not occurred even to Samuel Butler, who devised the ultimate nightmare of machines one day ruling mankind.

But as early as the eighteenth century there had been premonitions of modern automation. Perhaps the single most important of them was the "governor," James Watt's outstanding contribution to the "feedback" of present-day cybernetics. The Watt governor worked very simply on the principle of centrifugal force. A vertical shaft driven by the steam engine spun two arms with heavy balls at their outer ends. As the engine speed increased, centrifugal force raised the arms higher and higher, lifting a collar around the shaft. The collar connected with a throttle, or steam valve, closing it when the speed became too great. The steam engine could thereby "tell itself" to slow down or speed up.

In a sense, some industries mass-produced their products, but this meant only great numbers, not automation in the production line. The textile industry produced inexpensive and abundant fabrics, but it was not a continuous process, with the fiber going in one end of a machine and a finished product coming out the other. The raw materials—wool, which had to be sheared from a sheep's back; flax, which had to be grown and retted; cotton, which had to be hand-picked; and silk, which had to be unwound from a cocoon—needed laborious preparation (cleaning, carding, and spinning) before they could be woven. Then the cloth that the power-loom produced still had to be scoured, fulled, raised, cropped, frizzed, and bleached. In time, of course, machines that mechanically imitated human efforts were introduced at each stage, but all they did was mechanize craftsmanship. (A flying shuttle, for instance, replaced the weaver's arm and wrist movement.) One person could produce more of the same than before, but someone still had to operate the machine.

Gig mills, spinning jennies, cotton gins, and steam engines enormously increased productivity and efficiency in the textile industry. But this is evolution rather than revolution. "Revolution" implies a breach of the paradigm, a breakout from the framework of convention, or the overthrow of a whole dynasty of ideas. (The atom bomb was not a scientific revolution; the quantum theory was.) Fabrics are still woven on the principle of warp and weft used by the basket makers and fiber weavers of ancient times. The practical methods may change, the markets may increase, the fibers may now be synthetic, but the essential system remains. Penelope with her distaff must have made slow work of spinning. Samuel Crompton's "mule," a cross between Hargreaves' spinning jenny and Arkwright's water frame, had twenty spindles; today a modern "mule," which is a very close descendant of Crompton's machine, may work with up to 1350 spindles, but it works in much the same fashion. In the 1930's Lancashire cotton weavers went on strike because they were asked to mind eight looms instead of four; today hundreds of semiautomatic looms need the skilled supervision of only one man. The spinnerets of the silk worm have become the spinnerettes of man-made fibers. But a textile is still built up, thread over thread. If paper dresses can be made as soft and tough as some paper handkerchiefs, as absorbent as wool, and reasonably durable, the "fabric" we wear could be made in a continuous process, without any acknowledgement of the basket weaver. *That* would constitute a real revolution.

A SMITHSONIAN
PORTFOLIO

W*ith the coming of industrialism it was inevitable that the machine would reach the farm. In 1800 most food was still being produced solely by human effort. As the urban population began to swell, the need for farm machinery became obvious. Once begun, the mechanization of farming proceeded rapidly. The same farmer who had once goggled at the sight of a horse-drawn reaper lived to see, in 1901, the Huber Steam Tractor, below, replacing the horse. A revolution in farming was taking place, and several of its major inventions are shown on the following pages (all taken from the Smithsonian collection).*

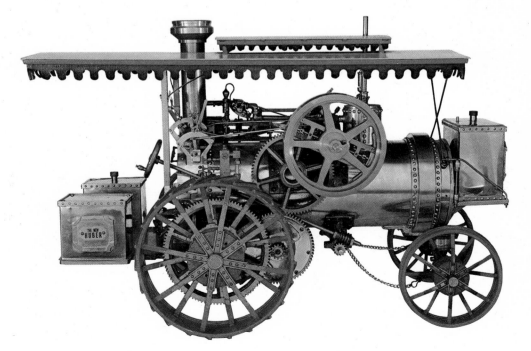

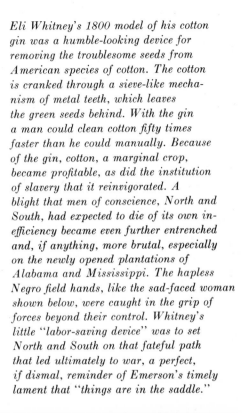

Eli Whitney's 1800 model of his cotton gin was a humble-looking device for removing the troublesome seeds from American species of cotton. The cotton is cranked through a sieve-like mechanism of metal teeth, which leaves the green seeds behind. With the gin a man could clean cotton fifty times faster than he could manually. Because of the gin, cotton, a marginal crop, became profitable, as did the institution of slavery that it reinvigorated. A blight that men of conscience, North and South, had expected to die of its own inefficiency became even further entrenched and, if anything, more brutal, especially on the newly opened plantations of Alabama and Mississippi. The hapless Negro field hands, like the sad-faced woman shown below, were caught in the grip of forces beyond their control. Whitney's little "labor-saving device" was to set North and South on that fateful path that led ultimately to war, a perfect, if dismal, reminder of Emerson's timely lament that "things are in the saddle."

On the right is a Wisconsin farmer, reaping his grain with an old-fashioned scythe, a tool perfected in the twelfth century A.D. Until Cyrus McCormick invented his reaper in 1831, an early model of which is shown below, cutting with a scythe severely limited the number of acres a farmer could work. McCormick's horse-drawn machine, with its blades working back and forth as the reaper moved, greatly decreased the amount of time required for reaping. His machine was made even more efficient by Obed Hussey, whose 1847 reaper (opposite) overcame one of the machine's few shortcomings—clogged cutting blades. The reaper was probably the most important invention in American agricultural history, having an immediate and dramatic impact on the national life.

Barbed wire, right, which consists of two twisted iron strands with coils set along its length, was patented in 1874 by Joseph Glidden. In the West it led to the building of fences. Cattle raisers no longer had to drive their herds over an open range; they could confine them more efficiently on vast private ranches, while wheat farmers found it useful for keeping out stray cattle. It greatly increased the value of western land, and with inevitable results. For the Indian and his buffalo there was no room left in this new economy. Angry and confused, Plains Indians like the Cheyenne, Wolf Robe, left, fought desperately and long but to no avail. Behind the new iron fences western farming and cattle-raising were growing ever more productive. By 1877, yet another key machine had been added to the farmer's equipment: Whitely's reaper, below, which raked as well as cut the grain. Machine-age man was now on the prairies for good.

Along tracks of freshly made steel, below, and in the form of the handy Frick Portable Steam Engine, left, Watt's invention had caught up with the farmer. In 1869 the transcontinental railway opened, and in the 1880's alone over seventy thousand miles of track were laid, and 90 per cent of the nation's rolled steel went into rails.
With swift locomotives to carry their produce and powerful tractors to haul bigger and better farm machines, the wheat farms of America became the breadbasket for a new world of cities, towns, factories, and more and more machines.

THE SPARK
OF LIFE

It is interesting to speculate what might have happened had Michael Faraday and Joseph Henry preceded James Watt. If early in the eighteenth century the world had been given electric motors and generators prior to the steam engine, then the self-evident primary power source would have been water; and because waterwheels were the prevailing power paradigm, hydroelectricity, not fossil-fuels such as coal, would have been the obvious way of producing cheap power, and countries with an abundance of falling water, rather than coal, would have had the decided advantage. David Livingstone simply would not have happened upon the Victoria Falls; he would have been out looking for it. The whole pattern of industrial power (and political and economic power as well) would have been quite different, and many of today's so-called developing nations would have been long since fully developed.

But the generation of ideas and the generation of electricity are, of course, vastly different things. Moreover, as we have seen, to make a machine, however ingenious one might be, one needs materials. The primary material of the early eighteenth century was iron, which was produced by burning coke, which was processed coal that had to be mined. As industrialization expanded and iron production increased, the demand for coal called for mining at depths where water seepages called for new kinds of pumps. And it was the creation of those pumps, and the development of an increased knowledge about pneumatics, that soon suggested steam pumps. Hence Watt and the world-revolutionizing steam engine.

In addition it was the climate of the prosperous coal-steam economy of the late eighteenth and early nineteenth centuries that was conducive to the kind of theoretical investigation that we call "pure science." Men such as Faraday and Henry could carry on their own work apart from conventional thought, or what was then the conventional, production-and-profit-motivated industrial technology.

Joseph Henry's base of operations at the Smithsonian Institution was quite literally the product of the coal-steam economy, for it was a bequest to the government of the United States by James Smithson, the heir to an English coal fortune, that made possible the founding of that celebrated center of scientific scholarship. Faraday, on the other hand, carried on his investigations at the Royal Institution in London, which, interestingly enough, was the creation of an American, that gifted and contradictory character, Count Rumford.

During the Revolutionary War, Rumford (then known simply as Benjamin Thompson) was opposed to the colonists' cause and moved to London. He had also been suspected of spying for the British, a suspicion later confirmed. He subsequently fought with the British army in America, and after the war went to Bavaria, where he became a count of the Holy Roman Empire. Politics aside, he was a thorough and observant scientist, and in 1799, again back in London, he founded the Royal Institution by raising private subscriptions for a lecture and research establishment that was to be concerned particularly with "the management

of heat and the saving of fuel and various other mechanical contrivances, by which domestic comfort and economy may be promoted."

The first director of the Institution was the great Humphry Davy, then a young chemist, who, apart from his many outstanding discoveries, is remembered for the Davy safety lamp that protected miners from the risk of blackdamp. Faraday, who as a bookbinder's apprentice had crept up the backstairs at the Royal Institution to hear Davy lecture, became first Davy's bootblack, then his inspired protégé. It might therefore be said that the founding of the Smithsonian by an Englishman was an instance of reverse lend-lease. But what is more to the point in our story is that the work of Michael Faraday of the Royal Institution, and Joseph Henry of the Smithsonian Institution, carried on independently yet simultaneously, marks another major turning point in the evolution of mechanical power.

Faraday was attracted to the subject of electromagnetism by the work of Danish physicist Hans Christian Oersted, who, in 1819, during a lecture at the University of Copenhagen, unintentionally placed a conducting wire near a simple mariner's compass. The needle immediately swung perpendicular to the wire. Because no one had as yet recognized the relationship between electricity and magnetism, the professor said nothing of it to his class lest he look a fool, but retired quietly to his laboratory to conduct further tests.

Just what did man know of electricity by then? Briefly, its history begins about 600 B.C. with the Greek philosopher Thales noting that

amber decorations on spinning wheels attracted threads, feathers, and other light objects through what we know as "static electricity." The Greek word for amber was "elektron," from which William Gilbert, a physician to Queen Elizabeth I, coined the word "electricity." In 1672 Otto von Guericke, whom we have already met as the discoverer of the air pump, set sparks jumping between metal balls mounted on a small contrivance of his making. Seventy years or so later came the first primitive condenser, which is an insulated device within which a quantity of electric charge can be stored. The "Leyden jar," as it was known, was put together at the University of Leidon, in Holland, by a Dutch scholar named Pieter van Musschenbroek. Once charged with static electricity it could release a considerable shock to anyone who touched it.

Then, in 1752, the concept of "positive" and "negative" electricity was demonstrated, ever so dramatically, by Benjamin Franklin's famous experiment with a kite. By sending the kite into a thundercloud and getting sparks from an iron key rubbed against a silk string, Franklin demonstrated that lightning is a discharge of electricity between objects of differing potentials. The clouds formed one "pole," the ground the other, just as in the case of the Leyden jar and the finger. (It should be noted also that Franklin was extremely fortunate that he was not killed by his experiment, as others were later when they tried it.)

Thirty years later an Italian anatomy professor, Luigi Galvani, thought he had uncovered what he called "animal electricity"

when he observed a dead frog's legs twitching as though alive from applied jolts of electricity. But the electrical charge came not from the dead muscles but from the use of two different metals (the steel scalpel and the zinc plate), as was soon shown by the work of another Italian, Alessandro Volta, who proceeded to make his "Voltaic pile" (the first electric battery), composed of pairs of copper and zinc discs separated by brine-soaked paper.

Then came Oersted, who, a year after his chance observation of the compass needle, published a paper proving that an electric current in a conductor created a circular magnetic field around the conductor. During that same year, 1820, French physicist André Ampére demonstrated the magnetic action of one electric current on another: if two parallel wires carry currents flowing in the same direction, they attract each other; if the currents flow in opposite directions, they repel each other. He also showed that a cylindrical coil of wire, charged with a current, acted as a magnet.

Michael Faraday, surely one of the true giants in the history of science, asked the question: If electricity can produce magnetism, can magnetism produce electricity? After nearly ten years of struggling with the problem he came up with the answer—yes.

Faraday had coiled two wires about an iron ring, with one wire connected to a voltaic battery and the other to a galvanometer, an instrument used to measure electric currents. When he turned on the current he noticed that the needle swung out briefly, then returned to zero; when he turned it off the needle did the

same thing in the opposite direction. Later he mounted a copper disc between the poles of a powerful magnet, and by rotating the disc, generated a steady electric current. He concluded that when an electric conductor continued cutting the lines of magnetic force, an electric current was generated (induced) in the conductor. What he had shown, then, was that when either the magnet or the conductor is moved in relation to the other, electric currents are produced. Faraday had discovered what today is known as the principle of induction. He went on to refine his work with narrower magnetic gaps, and used carbon brushes and revolving armatures with copper (electrical) and iron (magnetic) circuits. The result was the prototype of a generator, or dynamo, capable of manufacturing electricity on demand, but it would be another fifty years before a functional power station appeared.

Meanwhile, Faraday's American counterpart, the brilliant but relatively unknown Joseph Henry, had, by 1829, wrapped insulation (shreds of silk from his wife's petticoat) around copper wire and closely packed many coils of the wire about an iron core, and with a battery no bigger than the one Oersted had used in his classroom demonstration, he produced an electromagnet capable of lifting 3,600 pounds. The following year he devised a small, primitive apparatus that featured an electromagnet pivoted in the middle, with a permanent magnet under each end. When an electric current passed through it, the electromagnetic beam produced a rocking motion. It was the first electric motor. Henry, whose

independent work in electromagnetism actually preceded that of Faraday, called his creation a "philosophical toy," but its potential was obvious. Through pure science the groundwork had been laid for an entire new line of machines. Implicit in the idea of the dynamo (moving parts producing electricity) was the idea of the electric motor (electricity producing moving parts), just as the idea for the waterwheel had been implicit in the idea of a mechanical means of raising water.

During the middle decades of the nineteenth century, several abortive attempts were made to develop commercial electric motors. In Russia M. H. Jacobi operated a small boat on the River Neva by using a large electric motor powered by large and foul-smelling batteries. In England Robert Davidson achieved a speed of four miles per hour with his battery-driven locomotive, the *Galvani*. In the United States a Vermont blacksmith, Thomas Davenport, built his own battery-driven electric motors to operate lathes and drill presses. But none of these ever came to much. Batteries were an awkward, inefficient, and costly source of electricity, and there was little economic incentive to improve the situation, since possible backers had their money tied up in steam engines.

Until a more practical means of providing electric power than batteries was developed, electric motors, however advanced, would be of limited importance. But the potential was vast, for an electric motor could be virtually any size (unlike the steam engine which had to be big); the electric motor could also be moved about readily and switched on or off according

to need, thus supplying instantaneous power in large or small amounts.

But if the current was not battery-supplied, then it would have to be carried to the motor from a generator, and until a way could be devised to do this without great loss of power over long distances, the potential of the motor would remain largely dormant. This power loss was precisely the problem of the steady (direct) current produced by early power plants, such as that built by Edison on Pearl Street in New York City.

By 1888 a new kind of motor had been produced by a Croatian engineer, Nikola Tesla, who had once worked for Edison. Tesla roundly criticized direct current in a paper before the American Institute of Electrical Engineers (things were far enough along in the world of electricity by then that there was a call for such an organization), and advised that it would be better to use two or more alternating currents. With alternating current produced by a proper "transformer" (which had already been developed in England), the problem of power loss was virtually eliminated. In theory, electricity could be sent just about anywhere, and in a very short time it was. And so commenced the use of AC current, rather than DC, for heavy industrial purposes.

The same year that Tesla delivered his paper, the discovery of how to produce a rotating magnetic field by means of two currents had been made independently by an Italian, Galileo Ferraris. Then, almost immediately afterward, a German, M. von Dolivo-Dobrowolsky, used three different currents to produce a rotating magnetic field. The Tesla, Ferraris, and Dobrowolsky motors were known as "induction motors," because a voltage was induced in the rotor, or rotating member, by the rotating magnetic field. By the mid-1890's electric motors were on their way to becoming the motive means of the twentieth century, for by then George Westinghouse, who had been among the first to recognize and champion the virtues of AC current, had won a crucial victory over Thomas Edison in what became known as "The Great Power Fight." In 1896 Westinghouse was awarded the contract to build the huge power plant at Niagara Falls. It was, of course, an AC plant, thus inaugurating a new age of mammoth electric power.

The importance of the electric motor would be hard to overestimate. Today it powers everything from subways to carving knives; tomorrow it may power the family automobile as well, along with numerous other gadgets still unborn. But essentially the electric motor was, in the story of our evolving machine, a replacement for the steam engine. For all its many unique virtues it was still doing the job steam did, as can be seen clearly in the replacement of the steam locomotive by electrified trains. But consider those things that electricity could do that steam could not! Could steam have given us a telegraph, a telephone, or most important of all, a light bulb?

The development of electric light in a gas-dominated century had to overcome numerous roadblocks. Prior to his death in 1829, Humphry Davy, while using the voltaic battery as a source of energy for chemical analysis, had

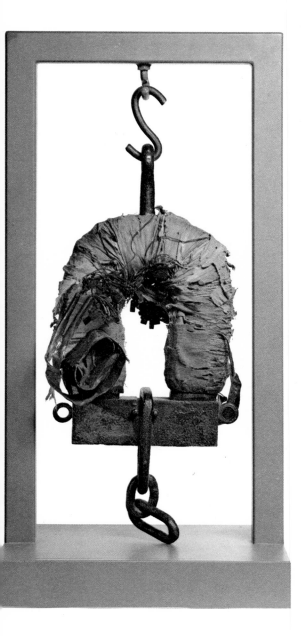

produced the carbon arc light by bringing two pieces of charcoal together and causing a flare of electricity to jump between them. The next two decades evolved several ingenious devices to produce a garish arc light. Sticks of carbon burned away so that they had to be continuously pushed together. W. E. Staite, in 1847, employed his "pyrometric principle": the heat of an arc increases as the carbon points move farther apart. In his invention this heat caused a copper wire to expand and to trigger a weighted gear that engaged a rackwork and raised the lower carbon.

Arc lamps were introduced into a number of English lighthouses, and in the 1870's they were introduced into French mills and the La Chapelle railway station in Paris. (The light was fierce.) In England R. E. B. Crompton introduced indirect lighting, and Paul Jablochkoff invented the "electric candle," which still employed carbon rods but required no mechanism. Zénobe Gramme, a Belgian, designed an alternating current generator especially for this high voltage arc light.

What the world was unknowingly anticipating was the incandescent lamp. Many had made filaments glow by passing electricity through metals that were short-lived because of oxidation. What was missing was the oxygen-free atmosphere possible in a vacuum. Soon after 1848 Joseph Swan, an Englishman, succeeded in making strong flexible strips of carbonized paper that glowed in an air-exhausted bulb. The light was short-lived because the vacuum was imperfect. Swan, however, reading of William Crookes' success in

producing vacuum tubes, and by using Hermann Sprengel's mercury pump, was then able to produce a successful carbon filament lamp at a meeting of the Newcastle-upon-Tyne Chemical Society in December, 1878. Five years later, after using mercurated cotton to make his carbon filaments, he used threads of nitrocellulose dissolved in acetic acid that extruded as fine threads through metal dies under pressure. This had only a temporary importance in improving carbon filament lamps, but it acquired a new significance twenty years later when it became the foundation for the artificial silk industry.

In 1877 Thomas A. Edison, at the age of thirty-one, announced that he was turning his attention to the incandescent lamp. He had already invented the ticker tape, the multiplex telegraph, the cylinder phonograph, and the carbon microphone. He had over a thousand patents to his credit but only one scientific discovery—the Edison Effect, which, typically, he patented. But he who made such good use of other people's scientific observations failed to recognize the significance of his own. (It was not the proper scientific moment.)

Even if he was not the man of the moment, he was surely the man of his times. In 1877 he was not waiting for divine inspiration; he was scouting about for an idea that would produce a profitable return. This is no jibe; it was what electricity, subjugated by the success and prosperity of steam engines and gas, had been needing. In all the battles of priorities in which Edison was engaged in his career, whether with Bell over the telephone, or Swan

over the incandescent lamp, he was a master of "public relations," and way ahead of the multibillion-dollar "crash programs" of a century later. He knew the value of beating the clock (and his competitors) by concentrated team effort. He did not wait for opportunities; he invented them.

While visiting a factory that made generators and arc lamps, Edison decided that there would be a great demand for a serviceable, mass-distributed lamp, with everything to go with it—generators, community transmission services, and domestic wiring. It was intuitive "operations research." He had to cost his product and his services to beat the powerful and entrenched gas companies.

He was looking for an electric candle that, unlike street lamps and factory lamps, would be within arm's reach and at the command of the customer. This meant parallel connections rather than a series. Each lamp would thus have the same voltage applied, and turning any number of lamps on and off would not affect the voltage applied to the others. In series the current in the lamp and in the lines is the same. In parallel the current in the line is the sum of all the lamps. Therefore, to avoid excessively large and expensive line conductors, Edison argued, the current in each of the lamps must be kept small. The filament must remain incandescent for a long time, but it must also have a high resistance.

Edison was not trying to produce a laboratory demonstration lamp, but a component in a larger technological development. He was going to offer the public and the financiers, not a product, but a package deal. He designed the base for the lamps, the wiring for the houses, the underground cable for the streets, the meter for measuring the supply to individual customers, and the generators.

When he switched on the lights at Menlo Park, New Jersey, on New Year's Eve, 1880, with all the ballyhoo of advance publicity, and a special train for notables from New York, he was presenting, in room lighting and street lighting, a working model of the system he was to turn on two years later from the Pearl Street power station in New York City.

Edison had an advantage. He had come into electricity through telegraphy. The electric telegraph had had a relatively fast success because it had no serious commercial competitors. In 1833, following Oersted's discovery of the deflection of the magnetic needle by an electric current, Karl Friedrich Gauss and Wilhelm Weber, working at the University of Göttingen, installed a telegraph line from the observatory to the physics laboratory (their respective departments), and sent messages over a distance of two miles. They had their own private "deflection code." They did not exploit it but a student of Gauss, Carl August Steinheil, did. He used two magnetized needles and made them move two nibs with little ink containers. The nibs printed dots on paper. When he was employed to install his telegraph alongside the first German railway, he proposed to use only one wire and to try to take advantage of the rails. Instead he found that the earth was a first-class conductor when two metal plates were sunk to subsoil water level.

Baron Paul von Schilling improved on the system by operating five magnetic needles, and William Cooke and Sir Charles Wheatstone adapted this idea by installing a panel with the letters of the alphabet and the numbers 0 to 9 on it, with the needles spelling out the transmitted message.

On the first of January, 1845, the London operator of the telegraph installed by Cooke and Wheatstone on the Great Western Railway received a message: "a murder has just been committed at salthill and the suspected murderer was seen to take a first class ticket for london by the train which left slough at 7:42 a.m. he is in the garb of a kwaker with a brown greatcoat on which reaches nearly down to his feet. he is in the last compartment of the second first class carriage."

When the train arrived at Paddington the man dressed as a Quaker (there was no "q" on the telegraph) was arrested. He confessed and Londoners looking at the telegraph wires said, "Them cords have hung John Tawell!"

But the year before, after having received substantial help from Joseph Henry, Samuel Morse had sent his famous "What hath God wrought" message from Washington to Baltimore, and it would be Morse who would see the idea of the telegraph for commercial use.

Samuel F. B. Morse was a Connecticut parson's son, who at an early age had become one of America's foremost artists. Returning from Europe on a sailing ship in 1832, he had been fascinated by the scientific conjuring tricks of a fellow passenger, a young doctor. One was a demonstration of the electromagnet. The idea

July 1st 1897

Chas Batchelor

James Adams

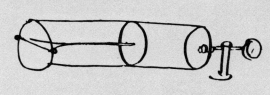

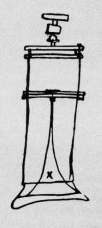

X vulcanite
B Thermos pile

X is a Ruller membrane Connected to the
Central diaphragm and the edge
being near or between the lips or
the act of speaking it gets a vibration
which is communicated to the central
diaphragm & then in its turn
Set. The outer diaphragm
vibrating hence the hissing
Consonants are reinforced to
make loudest the diaphragm
in motion we just tried
an experiment similar to
this thus

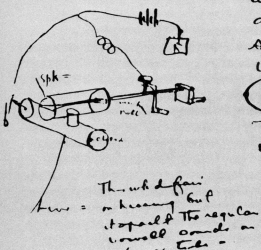

This whole affair
is hissing but
it spoils the regular
vowel sounds in
down talk

there = is hissing but

just tried experiment with a diaphragm
having an embossing point & held against
paraffin paper moving rapidly the
Sphy vibration are evident it nicely
& theres no doubt that I shall be able to
store up & reproduce automatically at any
future time the human voice perfectly

suddenly crossed his mind, as he recalled later: "If the presence of electricity can be made visible in any part of a circuit closed by an electromagnet, I see no reason why intelligence may not be transmitted instantaneously by electricity." The idea obsessed Morse to the extent that he abandoned his career as a painter and penuriously struggled to create an instrument and a system. He had, of course, to depend on batteries, a current too weak to travel very far; so he invented the system of "relays" borrowed analogously from the old mail-coach system of replacing tired horses at intervals. All the current had to do at the end of its limited range was to operate a small electric magnet, and thereby a fresh circuit powered by another battery took over. Another device, still unfamiliar, was his "key" for opening and closing the circuit at the touch of a finger. He also conceived the system of signals that bears his name, the "Morse Code"— a system of dots and dashes that, everything considered, was his chief original contribution. There was no reason why his system should not be successful, so he put it up to the United States Government, whereupon he ran into opposition from the Postmaster General and his postmasters. It was not until March, 1843, that the "Morse Bill" was passed in Congress, by a margin of six votes.

From there on telegraphy was a battle of wits rather than of entrenched obstruction. By 1866 the transatlantic cable had been laid from Newfoundland to Ireland. In the following year Charles Wheatstone introduced his high speed automatic system in which the punched

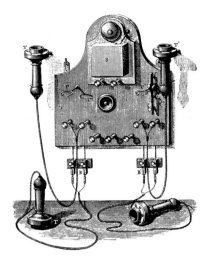

tape, with the holes spelling out the Morse Code, was fed into a transmitter that converted the holes into electrical impulses. Edison's multiplying refinements were therefore fed into an already profitable, highly capitalized, telegraphic system.

The first claim to the word "telephone" (far sound) was made in 1860 by Philipp Reis, a young German physics teacher of Frankfurt-am-Main. He made a wooden replica of the human ear that included a hammer, anvil, and tympanum. He replaced aural nerves with electric wires and when he connected two such ears with a battery between, he could hear faintly in one what was spoken into the other. He realized that he could not counterfeit nature, so he bored a hole in the bung of a cask and stretched bladder skin over it to act as a membrane. This was the first microphone. He tried to reproduce the signals by means of a knitting needle, wound with insulated wire and fitted into a violin. But his efforts impressed only his pupils, not the savants.

Nonetheless, the attempt influenced, at long remove in Edinburgh, Alexander Graham Bell. Bell's original interest was not commercial; he had devoted himself to the teaching of deaf-mutes. He pursued the idea and consulted Wheatstone, who told him of Hermann von Helmholtz, a spirit kindred to Bell's, because, as a physician, Helmholtz had entered physics through the study of the nerves and of the ganglia (which he discovered). Helmholtz had succeeded in making tuning forks resonate by electromagnetism. Bell found that when an iron diaphragm was made to vibrate close to a permanent magnet with a coil of wire round it, a weak current was induced in the coil, varying with the rhythm of vibrations. But Bell still had problems making progress with his device. "My inexperience in such matters is a great drawback," he wrote to his parents about this time. "However, Morse conquered his electrical difficulties although he was only a painter, and I don't intend to give in either." Bell, by then, like Morse, had also had the help of his friend Joseph Henry, who told him, "You have the germ of a great invention. Work at it." In 1876 in an attic in Boston, Bell used the instrument to call to his assistant on the ground floor: "Mr. Watson, please come here." Mr. Watson got the message.

On the heels of the telephone came still another device in the genealogical tree, Edison's "phonograph." Edison's interest in the idea was typical of his commercial outlook. He was not, in 1876, looking for an entertainment device. He saw the possibilities of a telephone system, not yet built, and he conceived the idea of a "telephone repeater," a voice recording that, like a telegram, could be transmitted in the absence of the speaker. (Think of today's answering service, or for that matter, all the "canned" radio programs.) He devised a machine in which the voice, vibrating a diaphragm that agitated a stylus, drew a picture of itself. This "picture" of grooves and indents "drawn" on a tinfoil sleeve wrapped around a horizontal cylinder could, by the reverse process of the stylus vibrating the diaphragm, reproduce the sounds either audibly or, as Edison originally intended, as electric impulses to

go over telephone wires.

Edison built the apparatus on a budget of eighteen dollars and patented it in 1877. Ten years later Emile Berliner saw that the up-and-down motions of the stylus on the cylinder must produce distortions due to gravity. His alternative was the "gramophone" and the "record," a wax-coated disc. He was also able to make copies. Once the sound had been recorded on the disc, a "negative" metal matrix was produced, from which any number of plastic "pressings" could be made. But it was not until 1925, with the introduction of the microphone, that mechanical recording gave way to electrical recording, eventually leading to the long-playing records of today that have three hundred grooves per inch, or enough to accommodate an entire symphony.

Related to all of this is the tape recorder. In 1898, Valdemar Poulsen, a Danish electrical engineer, invented what he called the "Telegraphone." He used two drums winding and unwinding steel tape or wire. He also suggested paper tape covered with metallic dust. A microphone, converting sound vibrations into an electric current, would act on an electromagnet, which would agitate the membrane to reproduce them. He also pointed out that it was an economical system because you could reuse the tape merely by demagnetizing it, by passing a steady current through the electromagnet. Poulsen was a jump ahead of history. Wire recordings were used in broadcasting between the wars, but the German magnetophone system, in which iron powder was embedded in thin plastic tape, came just around

the start of the Second World War, and was extensively used during the war. It had the advantage of immediate demagnetizing censorship while the speaker (even the Führer himself) was unaware that his live voice was passing through magnetophone surveillance.

The other major advance in sound recording came with the photoelectric cell. In 1887 Heinrich Hertz discovered the photoelectric effect (emissively) when he noticed, during his momentous radio researches, that when light fell on the spark knobs, the sparks jumped more easily. In 1873 Willoughby Smith found that the element selenium, normally a poor conductor, becomes responsive to current when light falls on it. This is the photoconductive effect. There is also the photovoltaic effect. It was noticed that if a layer of selenium is sandwiched between a layer of iron and a layer of gold, light falling on the gold sets up a voltage in the selenium; the iron develops a positive charge and the selenium becomes negative.

From those various effects came the photocell, which converts light into electric impulses and vice versa, so that it is possible to photograph sound and even put it on the same film as a moving picture.

It was a long way from the Leyden jar or Franklin's kite to the photoelectric cell, but it was a distance covered in a very short time as history goes. With the application of electricity to machinery, and more important, with all the totally new devices that electricity had given birth to, a very new age was emerging, at about the time when, according to the Western calendar, it was the twentieth century.

COURTSHIP
OF THE
MACHINE

We have become accustomed to treat *science* and *technology* as entirely separate things, and to erect about them a hierarchy of learning, a sort of intellectual class structure consisting of the following: pure, or academic, science; fundamental, or (as the French call it) oriented, science; applied science; technology; and technics. The first assumes that the inquiry has no purpose beyond the pursuit of knowledge for its own sake; the second has a sense of direction, but is a study in depth of phenomena that might have industrial applications; the third, applied science, is programed to produce specified results, such as a new commercial product; technology takes the laboratory findings and converts them into industrial hardware, flow-sheets, and production lines; technics gets the products off the line and maintains the machinery.

In the evolution of the machine, as in the biological process of intermarriage, it has been the crossbreeding between the sciences, and the espousals of the patricians and the plebs of science that have produced the spectacular results we see today.

A classic example of such crossbreeding was the Lunar Society of Birmingham, the existence of which coincided not only with the development of the steam engine but with the beginnings of the United States and the French Revolution. It was founded by Matthew Boulton, Erasmus Darwin, and William Small. It met every month on a night of the full moon (thus "Lunar Society" and the inevitable description of its members as "The Lunatics") so that Darwin could be lit home

The Bessemer converter of 1860, right, transformed steel from an expensive metal into the mainstay of modern technology. Essentially, Bessemer's process involves the removal of excess carbon from pig iron without the need for expensive fuel. Air is blown through the base of a converter filled with pig iron. As it passes through the iron it causes the carbon monoxide gas to burn off by itself, thus producing molten steel.

on his journey to Lichfield, and Josiah Wedgwood, the potter, on his way back to Etruria. No agenda or hierarchal ambitions restricted their free-ranging discussions. James Watt would dispute with Joseph Priestley about the true nature of his "dephlogisticated air" (oxygen), or argue music with William Herschel, the German bandmaster who became Royal Astronomer. Erasmus Darwin, when he was not propounding his views on biological evolution (well ahead of a grandson named Charles), might be telling Boulton how to improve on some new mechanical invention. Wedgwood could ignore Priestley's scientific perversity about the phlogiston theory and concentrate on the significance of oxidization, or go off in search of some nonferrous clays to replace his rust-colored pottery. Meanwhile, Samuel Galton (grandfather of Francis Galton, the pioneer of genetics) might be introducing Mr. Collins, the "rebel" guest from America, or Priestley might be heard reading his latest letter from Benjamin Franklin.

Also involved with this society were John Roebuck and James Keir, both medical graduates. Without Roebuck's commercial development of sulphuric acid, and Keir's alkali factory (the first in Britain), the multiplication of machines using steam power, and the processing of their mass products would not have been possible. Note also the fact that they were physicians, for medicals were often that bridge between science and common sense that we now call technology.

Science itself was revitalized by those *parvenus*. Admission into fellowship of men like Boulton, Watt, and Wedgwood reinvigorated the Royal Society, which, despite (or because of) Isaac Newton's presidency for twenty-four years (1703–1727), had become a society of dilettantes, an aristocracy of intellectuals.

It was just such a "miscegenation of the sciences" that gave birth to the atomic theory. John Dalton, the son of a weaver, was not a "university man" but a largely self-taught mathematician, physicist, and meteorologist. Had he been an academic chemist he would have been restrained within the prevailing paradigm and would not have conceived his "theory of definite proportions." Instead, his interest in the atmosphere led him to the study of the constitution of mixed gases. His analysis of air in 1801 showed that it was always composed of the same proportions of oxygen and nitrogen, with small quantities of water vapor and carbon dioxide. Any chemist could have told him that these gases are not in combination and have different densities. But why then did the heaviest not sink to the bottom and the lightest rise to the top? Unlike the chemists, Dalton could think physically. He could explain the behavior of the gases as though they were composed of minute particles of different size. If matter were composed of a large number of elementary, homogeneous, and distinct substances, themselves composed of indivisible and indestructible atoms, all atoms of any particular element would be precisely like each other but different from the atoms of other elements. He assumed that the combination takes place in the simplest possible way, with one atom of

one element combining with one atom of another. He realized also that in compounds higher ratios were possible.

Dalton broke with the prevailing paradigm and created a new one, within which nineteenth-century chemists could work, and within which Dmitri Ivanovich Mendeléev could produce his periodic table in 1869, arranging the elements by their atomic weights in relation to hydrogen, the lightest of all. Where gaps appeared in his table he predicted the properties of the elements to fill them. Chemists could thus look for them and very often actually discovered them.

These were the chemist's atoms, still indivisible but capable of combining in molecules in a recognizable way. For our purpose, they played a very important part in the evolution of the machine. They made possible the production of new fuels (the fractionation of oil) and the mastery of new materials. Metallurgy was no longer a version of Hittite ore-cooking. Réaumur, with his chemical approach to the mysteries of steel, had prepared the way for the controlled and comprehensible mass production of that alloy. By the middle of the nineteenth century Britain, then the world's greatest iron producer, was turning out about two and a half million tons of wrought iron but only sixty thousand tons of steel, then made by the slow and expensive "puddling" process. In 1855 Henry Bessemer developed a fixed, vertical "converter" through which air was blown from the foot—the blast furnace. His first results were unsatisfactory for two reasons: one was the loss of heat during the addi-

tion of the molten iron and the running-out of the molten steel; the other was that the steel was brittle and contained blowholes. The first was met by mounting the converter on an axis, which allowed it to be tilted for charging and discharging. The second was a problem for the metallurgical chemist, and was met by the introduction of spiegel, an alloy of manganese and iron, into the smelting process. This had a degasifying effect and removed the excess of oxygen. Also the deleterious effects of phosphorous were soon recognized and the carbon content controlled to produce different grades of steel. Now, both "mild" steel (replacing wrought iron) and "hard" steel (for cutlery and the like) could be produced quickly and at far less cost.

In the United States the first rail made of Bessemer steel was rolled in 1865. In 1863 the first steel-plated ship, the *Banshee*, crossed the Atlantic. In 1874 steel replaced iron in a part of the Eads Bridge crossing the Mississippi River at St. Louis, with the girders supplied by Andrew Carnegie's steel company. In 1888 the top four stories of the ten-story Home Insurance Building in Chicago had steel frames, and the age of the steel-girdered skyscraper was on its way. Elevators, without which such heights would not have been practical, had already been demonstrated at the New York Fair in 1854 by Elisha Graves Otis, who employed a hydraulic motor, pulleys and counterweight, and safety ratchets. By 1900 steel production in the United States had grown from twenty thousand tons in 1867 to over eleven million. About 1868 a British metallurgist, Robert

Two basic engines that steel made practical include the steam turbine, below, whose blades are rotated by the pressure of extremely hot steam, and the internal combustion engine, in which a piston is driven by an explosion of gases. At right is the basic four-stroke cycle, prototype of the modern automobile engine. Below is the rotor, or moving blades, of a modern steam turbine, an engine used since its inception in 1884 to power electric dynamos.

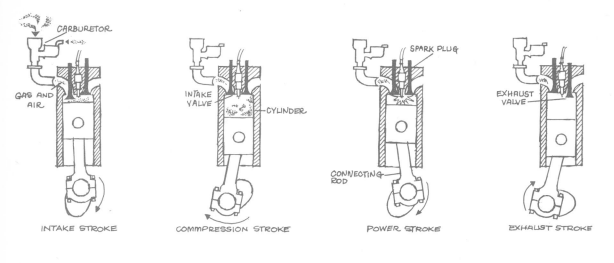

INTAKE STROKE   COMMPRESSION STROKE   POWER STROKE   EXHAUST STROKE

Mushet, discovered that by adding tungsten and vanadium and increasing the manganese in steel, self-hardening or air-hardening tools could be produced. They increased the cutting speeds from forty to sixty feet of mild steel per minute. High-speed steel, doubling that rate, came at the end of the century through the introduction of chromium. Such new alloys revolutionized the machine tool industry, not just through their inherent qualities, but because machine tool manufacturers had to rethink their machining processes to take advantage of the new possibilities.

Such new alloys also literally revolutionized the steam engine. It became possible to replace the piston rod with direct rotary power (a turbine) when metals became available that were sufficiently capable of resisting heat and of standing up to tremendous centrifugal force. With such materials British engineer Charles Parsons mounted a series of turbines, each consisting of a ring of blades arranged on a long shaft inside a fixed circular casing, which carried rows of similar blades projecting inwards between the rows of blades on the shaft. The shaft with the blades is called the rotor; the stationary casing with its blades is called the stator. With this series of turbines Parsons was able to use steam at its hottest and also through each of its cooling stages, until it eventually escaped at atmospheric pressure. He could produce the extraordinary speed of eighteen thousand revolutions per minute, and even in the atomic power stations of today, the turbine is still the best prime mover for producing electricity.

And it was, of course, the availability of low-cost steel that made possible that most characteristic machine of our age, the internal combustion engine, not to mention all the machine tools it takes to produce it, or all those millions upon millions of assemblages of steel, aluminum, and chromium that it powers over the world's highways.

The first internal combustion engine was built in 1860 by a French engineer, Étienne Lenoir. It was fired by coal gas. In 1884 an Englishman, Edward Butler, produced a gasoline-driven tricycle with a two-cylinder motor, incorporating a carburetor and a dynamo-produced ignition. He was thwarted by the "Red Flag Law" that had been passed by a Parliament dominated by railway interests, and which had restricted horseless carriages to a speed of four miles per hour on the open road and two miles per hour in towns. A man carrying a red flag warned of their approach.

But the recognizable grandparent of the modern internal combustion engine was the one built in 1876 by Nikolaus Otto, a traveling salesman from Cologne who had chanced upon a newspaper account of Lenoir's engine and then set about to improve it. Otto's engine of 1876 used illuminating coal gas in a single horizontal cylinder, which operated on the four-stroke cycle. On the first, or the intake stroke, the piston drew in a measured mixture of gas and air, which was compressed by the return (compression) stroke. At the point of maximum compression an open flame ignited the charge and the resulting explosion drove the piston through the third (power) stroke.

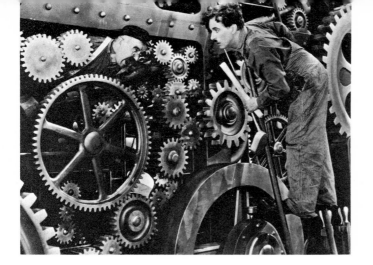

Man versus machine: Charlie Chaplin, portraying a relentless assembly line worker, confronts a nightmare of gears in the movie Modern Times, *a satire on mass production. The moving assembly line was born with the production of the immortal Model T Ford, right, which came in all shades of black. By combining two existing techniques, interchangeable parts and the conveyor belt, Ford developed a system that was efficient but monotonous.*

On the exhaust stroke the returning piston pushed the used gases through a vent. Because there was only one power stroke for every two revolutions, it had, like Watt's steam engine, to have a large and heavy flywheel to carry the engine along between the strokes. The piston rod turned a crankshaft that changed the reciprocating movement into a rotary one.

Otto's was a horizontal, stationary engine, but one of his engineers, Gottlieb Daimler, decided that it could be converted into a motor for road vehicles if it could only be made smaller and capable of developing power by reason of its high speed of rotation. Having decided what was wanted, Daimler proceeded to make it. He scrapped the use of illuminating gas and devised a surface carburetor that would enable the engine to run on vaporized gasoline. It was an ingenious contrivance, consisting of a vessel two-thirds full of gasoline, containing an annular float that was attached to a perforated vertical tube. Above this was a small reservoir for the carbureted air, from which the cylinder of the engine could draw its explosive mixture. As it did so more air was sucked through the vertical tube and bubbled through the fuel above the float, becoming charged with vapor to recharge the reservoir. Daimler also replaced Otto's naked pilot-jet with a hot tube that enclosed the flame. He upended the engine from Otto's horizontal position to a vertical one, and installed it on a bicycle in 1885. Thus we inherited the first motorcycle.

A year later Otto fitted his engine to a four-wheeled vehicle, one of the first automobiles. Unbeknownst to Daimler another German en-gineer, Karl Benz of Mannheim, was working simultaneously on a similar idea. He too had started from Otto's engine, but his model was water-cooled and included a novel ignition system—a battery, spark coil, and spark plug. This was not improved upon until 1902, when a high-tension magneto was developed to deliver a hot spark without the aid of a battery, and without moving parts in the cylinder. The Benz engine, capable of three hundred revolutions per minute, was fitted to a tricycle that, for cornering, employed the differential gear, patented in 1877 by Englishman James Starley. Benz also introduced the steering wheel and the steering column. In 1887, during his absence from Mannheim, his two sons, aged fifteen and thirteen, borrowed one of his horseless carriages and drove eighty-five miles—the longest journey such a vehicle had ever made, thus presaging the anxieties of parents forever after.

Daimler and Benz both went into the business of making automobiles and later merged. Britain, the pioneer of the steam age, was ten years behind Germany in exploiting the automobile market. (The "man with the red flag" was not abolished until 1896.) France, quick to realize the commercial possibilities of the auto, produced its own Dion-Bouton, single-cylinder, air-cooled engine by 1895. And America had Henry Ford.

Ford was a machinist in the employ of the Edison Company in Detroit. Apart from the merits of his car (a two-cylinder, four horsepower vehicle), which he built at home, his great contribution to the development of the

automobile was his commercial insight and organizing ability. He saw that the main fault of European cars had nothing to do with mechanics; they were designed for the well-to-do, for sportsmen, and motoring enthusiasts, not for the ordinary man or for the world's work. In 1899 he founded the Detroit Automobile Company and within three years was quarreling with his financial backers because they wanted expensive, luxury cars. He looked at a continent-wide country, with rough roads and muscle-dependent farming and saw the need for a tough, serviceable, internal combustion vehicle that would be priced for the average man. He was faced not only with the unimaginative caution of the businessmen, but by the opposition of those who serviced some eighteen million horses and mules of the America of 1900. With Barney Oldfield at the wheel, Ford's "999," built in 1902, could win races against other craftsman-built cars, but his real ambition was achieved in 1908 with the utility, mass-produced "Model T"—the immortal Tin Lizzie, which had little speed and was not especially handsome, but was rugged and practically foolproof. A kit of simple tools could keep it roadworthy; a village blacksmith could mend its back axle. From 1908 until 1927 the standard Tin Lizzie was sold to over fifteen million customers.

The importance of Ford in the evolution of the machine was not that he picked up the internal combustion engine, but that he successfully applied and perfected an old production technique—the assembly line.

There seems to be considerable question as to whether Eli Whitney deserves his reputation for having initiated mass production in 1798. At his Connecticut arms factory Whitney "broke down" the musket into component parts, designed special tools and jigs with which to make them, and thereby, according to many historians, introduced the idea of interchangeable parts. But elements of the system (it would become known as the "American system") had been tried in Sweden as early as the 1720's, and a uniformity and interchangeability of parts in the manufacturing of small arms were perhaps first worked out at the national armories at Harpers Ferry and Springfield, Massachusetts.

Nor was Ford the first to apply the system to building motor cars. Ransom Olds had built his "merry Oldsmobile" that way starting in 1899. But in any event, Ford put the idea to work on an unprecedented scale. He built a factory one-fifth of a mile long, on a conveyor belt system that synchronized the stages of assembly with the delivery of each part to the operator. Down the line came an automobile frame that slowly, piece by piece, was transformed into a finished car. The technique was such that the operator of "bolt thirteen" could not go wrong because bolt thirteen could not fit nut fourteen. Inherent in the entire process was scientific management, with its time-and-motion studies and production engineering. (Ford cars were very soon coming off the line at a rate of one every ten minutes.) Inherent in it also were workers' struggles, so effectively satirized in Charlie Chaplin's *Modern Times*. Many workers resented the impersonalization

of the individual and the lack of job satisfaction brought about by monotony and non-creativeness. Ford fought the unions to get his cheap, standardized cars, but he also compensated his employees by his second sound principle: the average man (the Ford worker) could buy a car only if he could afford it; to Ford high wages were thus, in the long run, good for business, so he set an example by paying his workers more than any employer had ever done before. His minimum wage in 1914 was five dollars a day, which was twice what most skilled workers were getting. A few years later Walter Reuther, head of the United Auto Workers union, reminded the president of another auto company of Ford's second principle. In a bargaining row the president of the company threatened to automate the entire plant, and also pointed out that machines don't pay union dues. Reuther countered by asking if machines could also buy automobiles.

With the increased production of cars came continuing improvements in the internal combustion engine. At the same time, improved gasolines perfected by the chemists added still more efficiency and power. Internal combustion engines were used for tractors and trucks, and a modification of the engine, the powerful and heavy diesel engine introduced by Rudolf Diesel of Germany, would eventually be produced for locomotives. But the great change would come, of course, when the internal combustion engine was applied to the proposition of getting man off the ground and into the air.

In 1799 a twenty-six-year-old Englishman, George Cayley, engraved on a silver disc, now in the London Science Museum, the diagram of forces involved in heavier-than-air flight. This was a miniaturization of his fundamental researches on aerodynamics. He maintained that the answer must be rigid wings. In 1804 he built the first glider and later made the first man-carrying flight. In 1809 he wrote, "It is only necessary to develop a suitable engine. Boulton-Watt's steam-engine might be a possible source of power, but as lightness is of so much value, there is the probability of using the expansion of the air by sudden combustion of inflammable powders or fluids." The type of engine that he prescribed but could not get was available about a century later. Icarus, who flew so near the sun that his wax wings melted, was resurrected. The moment had now come for the Wright brothers and their heavier-than-air machine.

The brothers Orville and Wilbur Wright, bicycle manufacturers from Dayton, Ohio, were men of method. They had decided to make an airplane that would be practical and not just an adventurous toy. They systematically collected all the available data on gliding (then in vogue) and analyzed the failure of other flying machines. After years of study and experimentation they devised a wind tunnel to test wing shapes and establish sound aerodynamic principles. They discarded the idea of the "ornithopter," the flapping wing of the bird, which men had unsuccessfully tried to imitate for centuries. Nor were they interested in the helicopter concept that had intrigued Leonardo da Vinci and the Chinese before him; rather, they were looking for a fixed-wing structure, so

Aviation pioneer Glenn Martin, opposite, appears more suitably dressed for a bicycle ride than a flight as he perches among the struts of a 1912 biplane. Below is the cabin of the Gemini V spacecraft, which in 1965 carried two astronauts on a 195-hour, 56-minute orbital flight around the earth. To master the spacecraft's complexities, carefully selected men must undergo long and specialized training. Yet the differences between modern astronauts and early pilots ought not to be exaggerated. Actually, the airplane depends essentially on more complex natural laws than does the Gemini V. The airplane exploits the intricate dynamics of air in relation to a moving wing, while the Gemini craft is simply shot upward with a speed that counters gravity. Historically, they both represent man's endless efforts to escape the ground.

they constructed three large gliders and thoroughly investigated the problems of controlled flight. They then built their own four-cylinder internal combustion engine and calculated the most efficient design for a propeller.

In 1903 the engine was installed in their research-approved design—a biplane with a wing span of forty feet, having an elevator rudder in front and a tail rudder with two movable vanes. Two propellers were arranged behind the wings in order to push the aircraft forward. It flew 852 feet in fifty-nine seconds.

"Faith in our calculations," wrote Orville Wright later, "and the design of our first machine, based upon our tables of air pressures, obtained by months of careful laboratory work, and confidence in our system of control developed by three years of actual experiences in balancing gliders in the air, had convinced us that the machine was capable of lifting and maintaining itself in the air, and that, with a little practice, it could be safely flown."

By 1905 the Wrights flew a distance of twenty-four miles. In 1909 Louis Blériot, a French engineer, flew the English channel in a monoplane of his own design. In another few years the airplane, in a variety of shapes, was at war in the skies over France, and in 1927 Lindbergh crossed the Atlantic, and aviation had come into its own.

But as early as 1913 a totally different kind of engine, a "jet propulsion" engine, had been suggested by a French engineer, René Lorin. It was an impractical idea, unless speeds of approximately four hundred miles per hour could be attained, speeds impossible for nearly an-other thirty years. Moreover, what has been said about the importance of alloys in the steam turbine is even more true of modern jet engines and of the aircraft they propel at supersonic speeds. Just as Cayley's aircraft could not fly without an engine using, as he predicted, "the expansion of the air by a sudden combustion of inflammable powders or fluids," so Frank Whittle could not have produced the jet engine without the metals to stand up to his exacting requirements. While in training as a flight cadet at the Royal Air Force College at Cranwell, Whittle conceived the idea of using a gas turbine for jet propulsion. Instead of individual explosions driving pistons in cylinders, he imagined the continuous burning of cheap fuel oil in a combustion chamber; the expanding gases would press against the blades of a turbine and make it turn. The function of the turbine was to operate a compressor, drawing air from the front of the aircraft and compressing it before it entered the combustion chamber. The hot, compressed gases would rush out of a jet pipe at the rear many times faster than hurricane speed and thrust the aircraft forward according to Newton's Third Law of Motion: *To every action there is an equal and opposite reaction.* Like the rocket, the jet does not "push against" the surrounding air; rather, it works like the recoil of a gun.

The idea of reaction propulsion was not new. In China, Wan Hoo, in approximately 1500 A.D., joined two kites together and propelled them with batteries of rockets. The rocket gun was used in several battles in the Napoleonic Wars. In the first quarter of this century Konstantin

Tsiolkovsky in Russia, Hermann Oberth in Germany, and Robert Goddard in the United States did impressive research on rockets.

Once aircraft designs were capable of speeds of over four hundred miles per hour, and once alloys had been developed to resist the temperatures of high-speed flight, jet engines made sense. Air speeds increased enormously until, in 1947, an American rocket plane, the X-1, broke the sound barrier. If an object travels at between 650 miles per hour and 740 miles per hour (the speed of sound) it overtakes its "bow-waves," which normally clear the way through the air ahead; if the propulsion of the plane is great enough, the air molecules can be pushed aside and supersonic velocities attained. Apart from the resulting sonic booms that upset people on the ground, breaching the sound barrier is also a great physical strain on the design and materials of any aircraft. Beyond that, at supersonic levels, there is the heat barrier. The friction of air, however tenuous, raises the "skin" temperature of the aircraft to tremendous temperatures. This again raises the problem of structural materials and suitable alloys.

For lesser velocities, aircraft construction has relied on alloys such as duralumin. Aluminum was a laboratory curiosity at the beginning of the nineteenth century. It is one of the most common elements in nature, but early attempts to prepare aluminum by chemical reduction failed because of its high energy of oxidation. Henri Étienne Sainte-Clair Deville managed, by chemical methods on a glorified laboratory scale, to produce it as a luxury met-

An artist's cutaway diagram of a turbojet shows the mechanisms of an engine capable of propelling an airplane 1,700 miles per hour. The broad row of blades, orange, known as the compressor, are rotated by the turbines at several thousand revolutions per minute. The whirling blades suck air into the front end, left, of the turbojet. As the air passes by the blades it becomes compressed to one-eighth of its orig- inal volume. It then passes into the combustion cham- ber, the hollow jacket that surrounds the central axis at the widest portion of the engine. There, a fuel is injected and burns, heating the air to 1,500° F. At such tremendous tem- peratures the air presses with great force against the blades of the turbine in the rear, turning them so rapidly that air is forced from the engine at enormous speed, thrusting it forward.

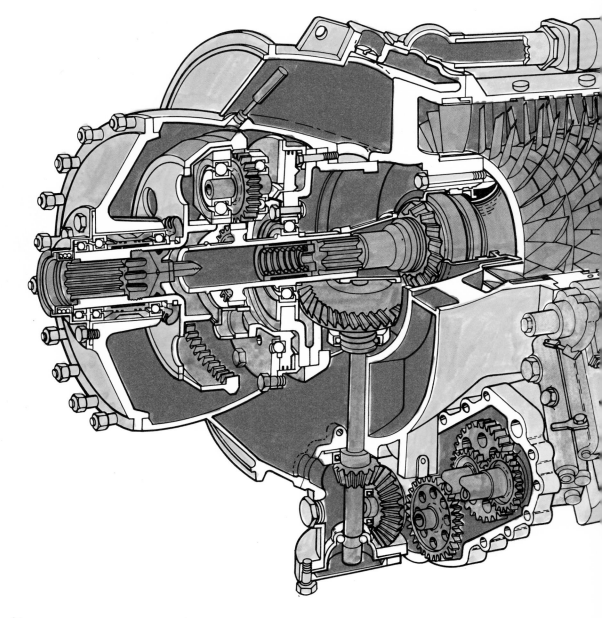

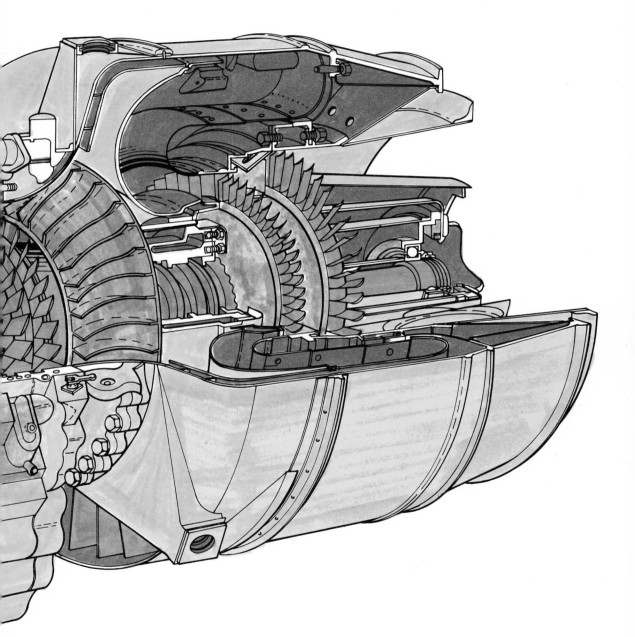

al (Napoleon III had cutlery made of it for state banquets); but the breakthrough came in 1886 when Charles Martin Hall in the United States, and Toussaint Héroult in France, independently discovered the process of direct electrolysis of aluminum. The aluminum ore (bauxite) is dissolved in molten cryolite, a double flouride of aluminum and sodium (originally found in Greenland but now manufactured synthetically), and an electric current is then passed through, carrying the elemental aluminum to a cathode from which it sinks to the bottom of the bath, where it is protected from atmospheric oxidation and from which it is drawn into vacuum vessels. Aluminum could become a useful metal, however, only when abundant and cheap electricity was available.

Electricity! How often the word keeps recurring in our story. Electricity to make aluminum; electricity to ignite the charge that powers the internal combustion engine; electricity to make day out of night. And in the second half of the current century, it is, as we shall soon see, electricity that is the vital force of totally new technological systems, which, seen in terms of the evolutionary process, are about as far from Edison's devices as Edison was from Cro-Magnon man. But it is back to Edison that we must turn to see still one other enormously important contribution of electricity—project research.

It was Alfred North Whitehead who said that the principle invention of the nineteenth century was the "method of invention." And nowhere was the method so neatly crystallized than at Edison's "invention factory" at Menlo Park, New Jersey. There, starting in 1876, Edison organized the first industrial research laboratory. He systematized the process of invention, coordinating the efforts of skilled mechanics, chemists, and even a mathematical physicist. The man who is so often pictured as a "loner" was, in fact, the originator of a team approach to research, which by itself was one of the very greatest of his inventions. As his biographer Matthew Josephson has pointed out, Edison's barn-like laboratory was the pilot model for the immense industrial research complexes such as the Bell System or General Electric Laboratories.

Edison's often cited belief was that genius was one per cent inspiration, ninety-nine per cent perspiration. And for him, in practice, this also meant the perspiration of many men possessing numerous skills. In a sense Edison systematized the kind of interaction of intellect that was at the heart of the Lunar Society. He brought men and methods together in one moment, and did it to meet the specific demands of the marketplace. Invention was no longer the private indulgence of the gifted amateur or the rare professional. Inspiration was no longer a chance affair. A technological methodology had been created to guarantee success.

Thomas Edison died in 1931. In another ten years the most momentous research project of all time would be under way, motivated by demands far more crucial than commercial interests. It would be the greatest of the great "crash projects," and after its work was finished the world would never be the same again. The stage had been set at Menlo Park.

THE SHOTGUN WEDDING

At precisely 5:30 A.M. on Monday, July 16th, 1945, a cataclysmic force at Alamogordo, New Mexico, made a notch in history from which the future of mankind would thenceforth be dated. Life on earth had suddenly and frighteningly changed. *Homo sapiens* had acquired a new source of energy, and with it the power to veto the evolution of his own species, and to turn his planet into a radioactive wilderness.

The Manhattan Project, a secret military mobilization of civilian science and technology, converted the laboratory discovery of uranium fission, made only six years previously, into a devastating weapon. Only a country as rich and resourceful as the United States, with its vast technological competence, could have produced conventional armaments for a global war and, at the same time, indulged in such a costly gamble involving rare skills, unfamiliar materials, and unpredictable results. And the gamble was not simply a matter of "whether," but "when"! Time, as far as the military were concerned, was the essential factor. And just as the sub-critical sections of fissile material were instantaneously brought together to produce the critical amount that exploded as the atom bomb, so the "bits and pieces" of science and technology were "imploded" to make the bomb possible.

Within just the last twenty years man has entered the Atomic Age, the Automation Age, and the Space Age. There is much truth in the current contention that of all the scientists and research workers who have existed from the beginning of *Homo sapiens* 90 per cent are

alive today. In other words, the bulk of scientific achievement belongs to the past fifty years and, mainly, to the post-World War II period.

The atom that John Dalton bequeathed to nineteenth-century chemists was conceptually different from the atom that exploded at Alamogordo. The latter was a thousand times more powerful than anything a chemist's atoms could produce, and also gave gigantic, mushroom proof that the word "atom" (from the Greek *atomos*, meaning indivisible) was clearly a misnomer.

In the 1870's William Crookes made a tube that he exhausted with a vacuum pump. In the narrow end he set a cathode, and at the bulbous end he placed a metal cross to serve as an anode. When the current was switched on "something" made the glass glow at one end. The rays proceeded in straight lines, as shown by the fact that the cross was silhouetted. They were not a form of light, however, because when Crookes introduced a magnet they were bent out of their path, indicating that they must be a "stream" of particles. His suggestion that they might be electrically charged particles could not be reconciled to the behavior of anything as big as molecules—clusters of chemist's atoms. Wilhelm Conrad Röntgen of the University of Würzburg followed up Crookes' discovery by studying the luminous effects that "Crookes' rays" had on certain chemicals. He enclosed the tube in black cardboard and completely darkened the room. When he turned on the current he discovered that a piece of paper coated with a luminescent salt glowed in the dark, despite the fact that

the cardboard was blocking the cathode rays. There must be "invisible light" coming from the dark lantern. When he was asked what he thought upon observing this, he said, "Think! I did not think, I investigated." If he had thought, at least within the framework of existing knowledge, he certainly would have stopped experimenting. This effect was against all the rules. He put a dense object on top of a sealed box, in which he had enclosed a photographic plate, and got an image. He used the masked rays to photograph the skeleton of his own hand, and thereby, in 1895, discovered X-rays, which we now know are produced when high-energy electrons lose kinetic energy in striking a target. But electrons had still to be identified, as they were almost immediately. J. J. Thomson installed a Röntgen tube at the Cavendish Laboratory, Cambridge, and directed his "boys," including Ernest Rutherford, just arrived from New Zealand, to study its effects. By a clever method, using condensed water drops on individual electrons, Thomson discovered that they had the same unit charge as that on the familiar ions found in salt solutions. From this he was able to calculate that the mass of the electron was $1/770$ that of the hydrogen atom. Although a more modern appraisal is $1/1822$, Thomson had showed that matter contained particles much smaller than the lightest atom, hydrogen, and that these particles were probably common to all the other atoms.

In France, Henri Becquerel prepared salts from that somewhat odd element, uranium. It had been taken for granted that the fluores-

An X-ray of a scientist's hand, taken in 1896 at London's Royal Society, confirmed Röntgen's new discovery of the strange, penetrating rays. That same year, Marie Curie and her husband Pierre, shown below in their Paris laboratory, set to work investigating the new phenomenon of radioactivity, a term coined by Madame Curie. In 1898 the Curies discovered a new radioactive element, radium, and showed that radioactivity comes from within atoms themselves.

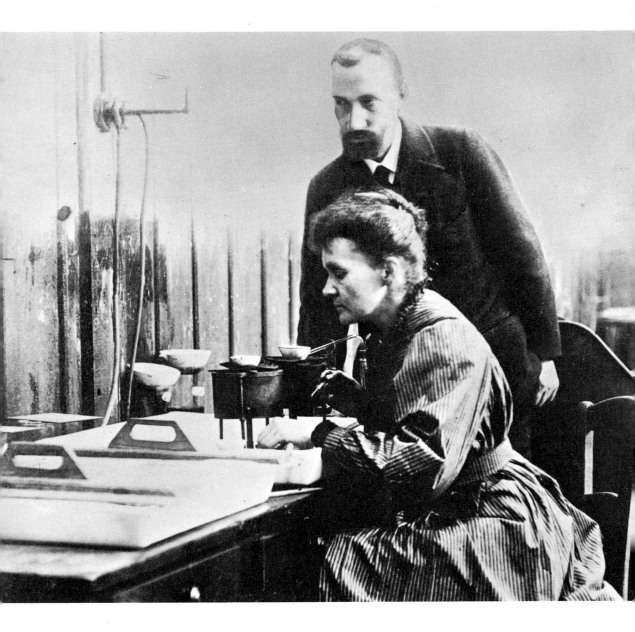

cence of this chemical was due to activation by light. He wrapped the salts in black paper and placed them on top of a photographic plate, and got the smudged shadow of the parcel. The salts were giving off rays powerful enough to penetrate the wrapping. He then found that the uranium itself was responsible for the strange effect, and not the light to which they had been exposed. Any uranium compound acted the same way. What Becquerel had uncovered was radioactivity.

Marie Sklodowska, a poor Polish student who had learned her science in the "Floating University" of Warsaw, a clandestine study circle of resistance to the Tsar, married Pierre Curie, chief of the laboratory at the School of Physics and Chemistry of Paris. Together they formed one of science's greatest man-wife teams. Marie undertook a study to see whether radiation was, in fact, an atomic property. She did not merely test elements in their pure state, she examined ores. In pitchblende from Bohemia she found sources more powerful than uranium or thorium (which she herself had discovered to be radioactive). In 1898 she and her husband isolated an element that was not in the periodic table (at least there was a gap); it was radioactive. She called it *polonium*. Their next discovery was radium, the most powerful source of radiation.

At about this time Ernest Rutherford had turned his attention to the exciting new field of radioactivity. He had asked himself why Becquerel's uranium and Marie Curie's radium atoms gave off rays. He used uranium rays as Thomson had used X-rays, to activate gases, and he found that there were streams of particles coming from the uranium atom. He labelled two of them A and B (from the Greek *alpha* and *beta*). They were definitely particles; the indivisible was being divided. The alpha rays were much less penetrating than the beta rays, because, for one thing, they traveled shorter distances—the difference between pea-shooting a ball bearing and a paper pellet. The betas were negatively charged and were apparently Thomson's electrons, but they were being fired off with much greater force from the uranium than from a heated filament—such as the difference between soot from a fire and cordite from a cartridge. The alphas were positive and had approximately the mass of a helium atom, which was almost four times the mass of the hydrogen atom.

At twenty-seven Rutherford was appointed a professor at McGill University in Montreal. With research students Frederick Soddy and Otto Hahn he investigated thorium and found that it changed into a new element, Thorium X; the immutable atom had become mutable. Within a few years Albert Einstein, a young official in the Swiss patent office, published his equation $E = mc^2$. At the time it did not seem very portentous, even to those who understood what it meant—that energy equals mass multiplied by the square of the speed of light, and that energy could be transformed into mass, or mass into energy. Nor did it seem to have any direct relevance to the atomic researches that Rutherford was simultaneously conducting in Manchester, to where he had transferred from Montreal. There he was joined by many bril-

liant research students, including Hans Geiger who, with Rutherford, invented in 1908 a sensitive detector for recording the emanations from the atom; Ernest Marsden was given the assignment of trying to find out whether alpha particles could be scattered through a large angle. Rutherford did not believe they could, since they were fast and massive. Marsden fired a beam of alpha rays at a thin foil of metal and made an extraordinary discovery: some were being scattered through an angle of 90°. Rutherford said: "It was almost as incredible as if you fired a 15-inch shell at a piece of tissue paper and it came back and hit you." For Rutherford it meant that the positive alpha particles were occasionally encountering a strong positive force and being repelled; most of the time, however, they went through. He could now imagine what became the Rutherford-Bohr model of the atom. The atom was largely empty, or spatial, like the solar system. The "sun" in this system was a positively charged nucleus, with negatively charged electrons orbiting at a distance.

This clarified many things. The chemist's atoms could combine into molecules, because the orbital electrons of one atom interlocked with the electrons of other atoms. The electric current generated by a dynamo pushed electrons out of the atoms of the conducting metal. Crookes' cathode rays were free electrons traveling in straight lines in a vacuum. The electric lamp glowed because electrons, disturbed in the filament, heated it into visible wavelengths of light.

The nucleus itself must consist of particles, since it ejected them as radioactivity. In 1919 Rutherford split the atom by bombarding nitrogen with alpha particles. In 1921 he insisted that, in addition to protons (the positively charged nucleus of the hydrogen atom, without its orbital electron), there must be neutral particles about the same mass as the proton, and positively charged particles about the same mass as the electron. Ten years later Carl David Anderson, at the California Institute of Technology, discovered the positron (positive electron), and James Chadwick, then with Rutherford at the Cavendish, proved the existence of the neutron, which, having no electric charge, was a kind of ghost proton that could penetrate a screen of electrons and ignore the positive repulsion of the proton.

Following the work of John D. Cockcroft and Ernest Walton at the Cavendish Laboratory, the first "atom-smashing machine"—the high-voltage linear accelerator—was built in 1931. It was a vertical cannon using protons as ammunition. Ernest Lawrence, at the University of California, developed the cyclotron, in which particles were accelerated and bent into a circular path and made to go around faster and faster. Now Einstein's equation was being put into a machine, for if particles were energized they would increase in mass. In January, 1934, Frédéric Joliot and his wife Iréne Curie announced to the French Academy, in the presence of her mother, Marie Sklodowska Curie, that they had reproduced radioactivity artificially by bombarding boron with alpha particles, thus creating the first man-made radioisotope. Italian Enrico Fermi, pursuing this line of research, started along the path that led eventually to plutonium.

Rutherford, then and to his dying day, was committed to his contention that the atom would always be a sink of energy and not a reservoir. What he meant was that on the evidence of the atom-smashing machines, the atom would always need more energy to split it than would be released by its splitting. A year after his death his former student, Otto Hahn, would prove him wrong.

In 1938 Hahn, with his colleague Fritz Strassman, at the Kaiser Wilhelm Institute in Berlin, observed that uranium when bombarded with neutrons yielded another element, barium. There were indications that the uranium was splitting into two parts and not just "fizzing off" nuclear particles. The significance of this was first defined by two Austrian refugees from Hitler, Lise Meitner (in Stockholm) and Otto Frisch (in Copenhagen with Niels Bohr). Meitner called it "fission" and showed that an invading neutron, disturbing the equilibrium of the nucleus, would cause it to divide (like a biological cell), and at the same time release other neutrons.

The apocalyptic significance of that observation was clear: if uranium fission could release surplus neutrons they could invade other uranium nuclei and produce a chain reaction; in given circumstances, that could mean an atomic bomb.

In 1939, in light of Nazi aggression, Albert Einstein sent a letter to President Roosevelt advising him of the possibility of constructing such a bomb. In England, a year later, ref-

ugees Rudolph Peierls and Otto Frisch drafted a convincing feasibility report outlining similar possibilities. But there were snags. The fissile atom of uranium is uranium 235, which in purified natural uranium occurs in proportions of only 1 atom to 140 atoms of uranium 238. It would be possible to separate the rare isotope by the mass spectograph, discovered in 1919 by Rutherford's colleague, F. W. Aston. In a curvature produced by a magnetic field, it would fling apart the lighter and heavier atoms so that they could be culled.

Once allied efforts were pooled by agreement between Roosevelt and Churchill, the United States launched a crash program to construct The Bomb. Nothing deterred it. The greatest scientists in nuclear physics became technologists, evolving new techniques and handling dangerously unfamiliar materials. At the Oak Ridge mass-separation plants science began to produce U-235 in quantity.

Simultaneously, Enrico Fermi, who had escaped from Mussolini, was working in a squash court under the stands of a playing field at the University of Chicago. He and his associates (the Chicago Group) were on a different track: if by some means the naturally escaping neutrons from U-235 could be induced to enter the nucleus of U-238, the results would be an artificial fissile material (plutonium). This was contrived by building a pile of graphite with a lattice of uranium rods. The graphite, like the cushions of a billiard table, would reduce the momentum of the fast neutrons and bounce them "back into play" with increased chances of their hitting and entering the U-238. It worked. As the inscription on the fence of the university's Stagg Field reads: "On December 2, 1942, Man Achieved Here The First Self-Sustaining Chain Reaction And Thereby Initiated The Controlled Release Of Nuclear Energy." Transferred to the vast production plants at Hanford, in the state of Washington, this process produced plutonium in quantity for the atomic bomb.

The nuclear reactor became the prototype for the production of a new primary source of energy for industrial uses. At a reactor station in Arco, Idaho, electricity from atomic energy was first employed in December, 1951. In June, 1954, a plant capable of providing enough energy for a small town became operative in Russia. In October, 1956, Britain's large-scale reactor at Calder Hall, in Cumberland, began feeding electricity on a commercial scale into the national grid, and Britain's program of atomic generating stations had begun.

A natural uranium reactor produces heat as well as plutonium. The reaction is kept under control by means of cadmium rods that act as "neutron gluttons," gobbling up any excess neutrons when thrust into the heart of the reactor. The heat is transferred by a coolant, such as water or even molten metal, to heat-exchangers. From there it becomes a job for turbine generators, which tame the atom into electricity for use in home or factory.

Shippingport, America's first full-scale power station, on the Ohio River near Pittsburgh, used ordinary water at two thousand pounds per square inch pressure as the coolant. Boiling water can also be used. The fuel element consisted of pellets of enriched uranium, which is natural uranium with an extra high proportion of radioactive U-235. Organic liquids can be used as moderators (in place of graphite blocks of the natural uranium reactor), and the fuel can be introduced in ceramic form.

In principle the most effective fission-reactor would be a "breeder-reactor," like the one at Dounreay in the north of Scotland. It is a pixilated pile that produces more nuclear fuel than it consumes. It is also a fast reactor, in which the neutrons from a "furnace" of enriched fuel are surrounded by a blanket of susceptible material. U-238 is converted into plutonium; thorium can similarly be converted into U-233, which is another fissile isotope of the element.

Despite the fact that massive, atomic-energy electricity plants have been built to feed into grid-systems, and despite the great variety of reactors that have been developed, the promises held out at the first International Conference on the Peaceful Uses of Atomic Energy in 1955 have not been fulfilled. The hope was to provide "foot-loose energy" for "power-hungry," underdeveloped countries, which needed small scale "packaged reactors" to develop their own industries. Reactors more compact than giant power stations have been installed in submarines—such as the first nuclear powered one, the *Nautilus*, which sailed 62,500 miles using up no more than eight pounds of uranium—and in surface ships like the Soviet icebreaker *Lenin*, and the American merchant ship *Savannah*. A general "share-out," however, has not occurred, mainly be-

Albert Einstein
Old Grove Rd.
Nassau Point
Peconic, Long Island

August 2nd, 1939

F.D. Roosevelt,
President of the United States,
White House
Washington, D.C.

Sir:

Some recent work by E.Fermi and L. Szilard, which has been communicated to me in manuscript, leads me to expect that the element uranium may be turned into a new and important source of energy in the immediate future. Certain aspects of the situation which has arisen seem
to call for watchfulness and, if necessary, quick action on the part
of the Administration. I believe therefore that it is my duty to bring
to your attention the following facts and recommendations:

In the course of the last four months it has been made probable -
through the work of Joliot in France as well as Fermi and Szilard in
America - that it may become possible to set up a nuclear chain reaction
in a large mass of uranium,by which vast amounts of power and large quantities of new radium-like elements would be generated. Now it appears
almost certain that this could be achieved in the immediate future.

This new phenomenon would also lead to the construction of bombs,
and it is conceivable - though much less certain - that extremely powerful bombs of a new type may thus be constructed. A single bomb of this
type, carried by boat and exploded in a port, might very well destroy
the whole port together with some of the surrounding territory. However,
such bombs might very well prove to be too heavy for transportation by
air.

The United States has only very poor ores of uranium in moderate
quantities. There is some good ore in Canada and the former Czechoslovakia,
while the most important source of uranium is Belgian Congo.

In view of this situation you may think it desirable to have some
permanent contact maintained between the Administration and the group
of physicists working on chain reactions in America. One possible way

cause of distrust, expense, and because nuclear engineers have not come up with a general-service reactor that would be to the generation of power what Henry Ford's Model T was to transportation.

Another long-deferred promise of the U.N. conference in 1955 was the prospect of thermonuclear energy, or "the garbing of the H-bomb in civilian dungarees." The H-bomb, with energies a million times greater than any chemical explosive, is the result of the fusion, not the fission, of atoms. This is how the sun generates its tremendous energy. It builds up from the lightest atom, hydrogen (mass 1), to helium (mass 4). The sun, with billions of years in which to do it, does the conversion by a complicated process, but for our purposes the simplest way to think of it is as the welding together of two atoms of deuterium. The mass of this double-hydrogen is 2.0162, and the mass of helium is 4.0038. As can be seen, there is a difference of mass between the doubling of the deuterium atoms (4.0324) and helium of 0.0286. Translated into the $E = mc^2$ principle, that is accounted for as energy, a mighty lot of energy indeed!

The welding of nuclei is by heat, such as is generated in the furnace-heart of the sun. Such heat can be reproduced on earth in the instant of the explosion of the fission-bomb (plutonium or U-235). The H-bomb was contrived by using a fission-bomb as the core, surrounded by hydrogen-atom material. The detonation of this core produced the desired fusion.

Controlled fusion is exceedingly more difficult. The heat for the flash welding has to be

many times the temperature of the sun, since it has to be accomplished in an infinitesimally shorter span of time. Where are the terrestrial materials to contain such heat? The British, Americans, and Russians have all coyly hinted that they are working on it. Each had their own ideas about how it could be done. Each depended on a practice well-known to lighting engineers—the passage of charged gases through tubes, as in neon-lighting—but they required a far greater understanding of plasma-physics, a science in itself. "Plasma," means a flux of atomic nuclei and their separated electrons. If they can be accelerated they will generate fantastic heat, which, as Francis Bacon said nearly four centuries ago, is motion and nothing else. Such heat, however, must be kept away from the material sides of any container, and if a beam wobbles and touches, all is lost. But a beam responds to a magnetic field (remember Crookes bending his cathode rays) and can thus be used to keep the plasma on a straight path until the heat generated by the movement produces the welding, and hence the thermonuclear energy. As George Thomson, the Nobel Prize-winner (son of Nobel Prize-winner J. J. Thomson), early pointed out, this system could produce electricity directly, without heat transfer or turbine generation.

Plasma-engineering has already produced the magneto-hydrodynamic (MHD) generators and motors. A very hot gas, when in motion, conducts an electric current. When it passes through a vertical magnetic field the particles (ions) are moved horizontally and can be collected by electrodes. And just as the MHD generator is related to the electromagnetic generator, so the MHD motor is related to the electric motor. It provides propulsion (like the "gunning" that changes the direction of a spaceship) by accelerating a jet of particles.

Systems of Nuclear Auxiliary Power, or SNAP, has provided still another source of electrical energy. It is a by-product of nuclear research, encouraged by that other "crash program" —space research. For example, a core of polonium (Marie Curie's discovery) emitting about two thousand curies of radiation will produce from 3 to 3.5 watts of electricity. In a small unit weighing about four pounds, the splitting atoms in the core produce heat. Around the core are grouped thermocouples, which are connected with a cold surface on the outside of the device. As a result of dissimilar temperatures and dissimilar metals, a sustained current is produced. There are eight different isotopes that can be usefully employed in this way, including radiostrontium. Radiostrontium would go on producing electricity in the thermocouples for at least twenty-six years. The wattage produced from a four-pound core would be the equivalent of a roomful of chemical batteries. Its usefulness to space engineers is immense.

Another source of power invaluable in space research is the sun itself. The sun is generous with its abundant energy—the source of all life on earth—but its rays are diffused. Efforts have been made to reconstitute the diffused rays—from Archimedes' burning glass to the modern use of reflectors to smelt and refine delicate metals—but even the best, including the ingenious "solar pool" at Sodom, on the Dead Sea, cannot produce power in real quantity at an economic cost. But if expense were not an obstacle, here would be an effective way of turning the sun's rays into electricity.

Reference has been made to semi-conductors. They can provide a "solar battery." When the sun strikes a wafer of silicon or germanium crystal, an electric current is generated. The light-waves jolt the orbital electrons of the elemental atoms out of position so that they can be collected. The first such battery contained four hundred silicon cells and was able to produce a 12-volt current. They provide the power for the radio transmitters and telemetering equipment of the space satellites. With the research and development costs written off by the space program, and with the experience gained, maybe one day such batteries will be cheap enough to become a commonplace source of energy in countries that have plenty of sun but little motive-power.

Another possibility is the fuel-cell, which may be described as a device by which chemicals are used for the direct production of electrical energy—the reverse of electrolysis, which has been referred to as a method of extracting metals; in its simplest form a current of electricity, passed through water, splits it into its constituents, hydrogen and oxygen. Conversely, the interaction of hydrogen and oxygen will produce water and current. Early experimenters were discouraged because the system did not produce currents in appreciable

The mathematical formula, right, taken from the scratchpad of nuclear physicist Richard Feynman, represents one step in the current search for the ultimate particle in nature, whimsically termed the "quark." With the atom now split into hundreds of subatomic particles, theoreticians hope to find an indestructible particle that underlies all the known ones, and thus give simplicity to theory, if not to the world.

$$\bar{\varphi} M_z \varphi = [a_1^* c$$

amounts, but an English chemist, Francis T. Bacon, revived interest by suggesting that it might become a method for storing electricity as a gas. Base-load stations and off-peak loads provide problems for generating-engineers. Nuclear and hydroelectric power stations are "baseload"; they work continuously and cannot be switched on and off like diesel generators. There are peak demands when everyone wants to use their electrical devices, as there are nighttime, off-peak, non-demand periods. One way of utilizing excess power is with a "pump-storage," which recalls Boulton's idea of taking the tailrace of a waterwheel and pumping it back into the dam. But fuel-cells can be used as lightweight, portable storage batteries by using the excess power to separate hydrogen from oxygen. Two electrodes, porous flat plates made from nickel powder, are suspended in a 40 per cent solution of potassium hydroxide and fed separately with compressed hydrogen and oxygen. The water formed from the gases comes off as steam. A standard car battery is rated at 8 to 10 watt-hours per pound weight. Fuel-cell batteries have an efficiency of from 250 to 300 watt-hours per pound weight. For transport purposes they have the advantages of being silent-running and having no harmful exhaust fumes. Electric automobiles might someday call in at service stations to replace their fuel-batteries with no more trouble than is involved in refilling the tank of an internal-combustion vehicle. And no smog!

Geothermal energy is another hope for the power-impoverished. This is the heat gener-ated in the crust of the earth. It releases itself violently from active volcanoes; it reveals itself in geysers of hot water, in bubbling mudpools, or as hot gases escaping from fissures of rocks. But those are only visible evidences. In Iceland, California, New Zealand, and Italy, this heat has been harnessed to the generation of electricity. The hot water and steam jets at Larderella, Italy, generate enough electricity to serve a populace of two million. It has been found that drillings into the formations associated with volcanic structures (not necessarily active on the surface) release steam or gases twenty times hotter than the natural vents, partly due to the friction of small-bore pressures. If we look at the volcanic arcs we shall see that they stretch, on the west, from Alaska down the west coast of Canada, the United States, Mexico and the whole of Latin America to Tierra del Fuego; on the east, from Kamchatka, through Japan and the Pacific Islands to New Zealand. Then there is the twin arc stretching from Iceland down the north and south Atlantic and into the Indian Ocean. There is the Great Rift, from the Dead Sea through eastern Africa. If modern technology could selectively and systematically tap this geothermal energy, it would provide that power that developing countries require.

In spite of the historical fuss about the discovery of the wheel there are those who now propose to abolish it—not only the electronic engineers with their obsessive objection to mechanical parts, but the mechanical and transport engineers as well. We recall that the great advance represented by the wheel was that it

$$- a_2^* c_2^* + a_1 c_1 - a_2 c_2]$$

reduced the area of friction, from the drag of a flat object like a slab of stone, to the narrow rim and small contact point of the rotating wheel. Now it is possible as well as practical to abolish friction. In the case of the hovercraft, this is achieved by traveling on a cushion of air. In the case of the linear motor, the vehicle is levitated by a magnetic field.

A hover cushion is the flattened out equivalent of a gas-bearing, in which the oil film (to reduce friction) between the rotating shaft and the bearing is replaced by air or other gas at high pressure. To float a body at a distance of three feet from the ground (as in the hovercraft) requires a considerable amount of power. Even when the cushion of air is enclosed by a "skirt," the wastage of pump-produced air is considerable, causing a disturbance in all the loose matter in the vicinity of the draft. This is the power-penalty imposed by large gaps between the vehicle and the ground (or water), which is unavoidable in riding over waves, rocky beaches, and rough ground. On a precisely prepared, smooth track the hover principle becomes much more economical. The gaps between the air pads and the wheels can be one-half of an inch or less.

Linear induction motors could produce a wheelless train, sustained by air jets and capable of high speed. Induction motors operate through the medium of a moving magnetic field. The "moving" field is, in fact, stationary, and is produced by a system of coils encircling a shaft and causing it to turn. But it could be produced by the system being flattened out, so that instead of making an axle turn, the induc-tion will cause a forward movement. An analogy can be made with a series of electric light bulbs arranged in a row, with only the first one lit. Then, as that first one is switched off, the second is switched on, and so forth. If this process is carried out very rapidly, the visual effect is of a quick spot of light traveling along the row. In the same way, if a row of electric magnets are arranged to be switched on and off in sequence, the magnetic field they produce appears to travel along a similar path. The induction motor makes use of a similar effect. Instead of switching on and off electromagnets suddenly, the process is carried out smoothly by supplying the electromagnets with alternating current. This magnetic system can be arranged in a straight line, capable of moving conducting objects forward. In the proposed railway system a pair of linear, motor-coil arrangements are mounted on the vehicle so that they are situated on either side of a central plate of aluminum, which is bolted to the track. Only half of the motor (as distinct from the rotary system) is carried on the vehicle, the other part being the track itself. So the weight of the power system is thus reduced by 50 per cent. The use of a linear motor makes possible a system in which the train runs on a cushion of air along the track, thus eliminating all wheels. Electrically, the faster the linear motor the better it is.

The first thing that all industrial development requires is an energy source to provide the power to motivate the machines. With this, one can then go shopping in the vast supermarket of technological science.

ALL SYSTEMS—GO!

With the flick of a switch the modern industrial worker can summon electron slaves to do prodigies of work that no human being would even attempt. The ordinary housewife has in her domestic gadgets more servants than the most ostentatious aristocrat employed fifty years ago. In his machine shed today's farmer has many more slaves than were ever owned by the greatest plantation owner. The average car of today has about two hundred horses safely stabled under its hood. This power is indispensable to mechanical progress and to the wealth it produces. It is an index to the wealth of any country, and helps explain why the per capita income of the United States is one hundred times higher than that of India, where power is still predominantly dependent on the strength of man and beast. It is sadly ironic that the poor can afford only the most expensive power, since food calories cost twenty times more per unit than the electricity generated from an atomic power station.

In the evolution of the machine up to the post-World War II period, electricity had been the main source through which energy was converted and delivered. Whether the primary source was wind, water, sun, or the atomic nucleus, it was electricity that gave the machine its breath of life. And now through the marriage of science and engineering, electricity has become "electronics," combining theory design with the many devices using electron emission or absorption.

The Second World War revolutionized the field of electronics. The imperatives of sheer

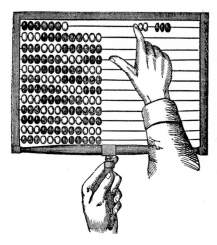

survival once again challenged man's creativeness, and once again, out of the ashes of human suffering and death, came astonishing scientific and technological advances. The sobering truth is that the urge to destroy, or to avoid being destroyed, had so accelerated the evolution of the machine that the time between idea and application had shrunk from centuries to decades, to years, to months. The laboratory studies that produced a vast system of military defense led also to a revolution in the refinement and miniaturization of the machine. At the end of the war there were surpluses—enormous stockpiles of unused materials and devices just waiting for peacetime technology to exploit them.

The history of radar development illustrates how war can be the stimulus for invention. As early as 1887 German physicist Heinrich Hertz demonstrated the reflection of rays by metallic objects. In time they became classified as radio waves. In 1925 Gregory Breit and Merle Tuve of the Carnegie Institution used radio pulses (squirts of energy) to measure the height of the ionosphere, a region that had been defined earlier by Edward Appleton. The din of German war trumpets spurred Englishman Robert Watson-Watt to make radar a practicable means of defense. Some of his British associates felt that an actual "Death Ray" might be developed, but Watson-Watt dismissed the idea and focused his attention on making radio waves detective. A crash program followed, and by the time of the Battle of Britain a radar system was detecting incoming Nazi planes and saving countless lives. To be applied offensively, the radar system had to undergo a process of miniaturization. Tiny valves and power systems had to be created. They made possible blind bombing when reflected waves gave a picture of the target on a cathode-ray screen. Since the war radar has been used for more peaceful purposes, notably in weather forecasting and in the surveillance of air traffic in cross-country flights.

The proximity fuse was another war-stimulated step towards miniaturization. It was a device that enabled a shell to "home" in on a target and explode within a desired distance from it. In military jargon, it turned many a near "miss" into a "kill." The war also witnessed the invention of the radio fuse and the photoelectric proximity fuse, both of which were very important in increasing bombing accuracy. The latter invention evolved into miniaturized and durable photoelectric cells, which, after the war, became invaluable in research and the development of television and cinema by converting light waves into electric signals.

War produced another change; it conscripted talent. Scientists who had been quite content to pursue knowledge for its own sake (like the nuclear physicists investigating the nature of matter) were suddenly summoned from their laboratories to put that knowledge to work. Not only did they find themselves working with technologists, but they also became involved in decision-making. This added a new dimension to industrial enterprise. Scientists supplied the "know-why," and the technologists the "know-how." In turn, the engineers

Progress in automatic thinking:
the ancient abacus, left, is a
digital computer in which
the position of a bead indicates
its numerical value, thus
providing a mechanical "memory"
for its operator. Below,
fourteen mechanical probes
carry out, under the control
of a computer, a factory inspec-
tion of integrated circuits,
each no larger than a pinhead.
The computer is programmed
to announce any flaws that the
probes might discover.

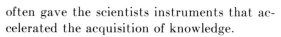

often gave the scientists instruments that accelerated the acquisition of knowledge.

Of all the many electronic devices stemming from wartime technology, perhaps the most important was the one that catapulted us into the age of automation and cybernetics—the electronic computer. The first ever constructed was at the University of Pennsylvania (under the supervision of U.S. Army Ordnance). It was called ENIAC, for "Electronic Numerical Integrator and Computer." It was put to use in 1946 in ballistics calculations.

The evolution of the computer, however, involves a long history, extending back to the ancient abacus with its sliding counters. The first truly automatic computer was designed in 1642 by Frenchman Blaise Pascal. His machine consisted of a series of cogged wheels numbered 0-9 that, upon turning, were able to add and subtract. (The mileage indicator on an automobile operates on the same principle.) A few decades later Wilhelm von Leibnitz advanced the computer a step further by arranging the wheels so that they could multiply and divide as well. But it required almost two more centuries before another major improvement was made. In 1850 an American inventor, D. D. Parmalee, patented a device that eliminated the inconvenience of turning the geared wheels by hand. His invention required the operator simply to push a set of keys, an innovation that can be easily recognized in old-fashioned cash registers.

In 1868 French engineer Léon Farcot devised an automatic control for a steamship rudder. It consisted of an instrument that ei-

50	33	33	32	32	32	33	33	33	33
51	33	33	32	32	32	33	33	33	33
52	48	16	16	48	48	16	16	48	48
53	32	32	33	33	33	33	33	33	34
54	32	32	32	33	33	32	33	33	33
55	32	31	32	32	32	32	32	33	34
56	32	32	32	32	32	32	32	33	34
57	32	32	32	33	32	33	32	33	33
58	32	31	32	32	33	32	33	32	33
59	32	31	32	32	32	34	32	33	33
60	32	32	32	33	32	33	33	32	32
61	32	32	32	32	32	32	32	32	33
62	56	8	8	8	8	8	8	24	8
63	32	32	32	32	32	32	33	32	33
64	31	31	32	32	32	32	33	33	33

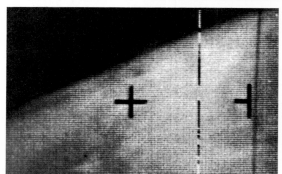

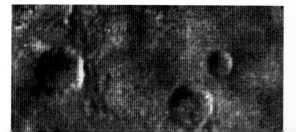

ther opened or closed the ship's steam valve, depending on the desired position of the rudder. He called his device a "servomechanism." It utilized the principle of the feedback, or error-adjustor, that is natural in most living things. In a sense Farcot's invention was the first step on the road to automation. It is the computer, however, that makes full automation truly possible.

For nearly a century the evolution of the computer stagnated, despite the diligent efforts of one Charles Babbage, an English inventor. He imagined an analytical machine that would be able to perform almost every mathematical operation. Using perforated cards, built-in memory devices, and automatic adjustments, Babbage labored with his brainstorm for thirty-seven years, all in vain. He died a defeated and poor man, far ahead of his time but having fallen just short of that vital scientific moment which, in this case, was World War II and the invention of the ENIAC machine. The computer, like the servomechanisms, had been waiting for electronics.

Thousands of machines have proliferated from the original ENIAC. Computer-scientist Howard Aiken once said wistfully, "I once knew everyone in the computer field by their Christian names; now I cannot memorize the names of all the machines." They have become incredibly more complicated, more efficient, faster, and with a logical capacity and "memory" far beyond the limitations of the human brain. And as they have become greater in capacity and versatility, they have become proportionately smaller. Thermionic valves have

been replaced by transistors, and memories can now be made even from tiny beads of compressed ferrite powder.

Basically, there are two kinds of electronic computers: digital and analog. Digital machines work only with the binary numbers 0 and 1. The numbers 0, 1, 10, 11, 100, 101, 110 in the binary system correspond to 0, 1, 2, 3, 4, 5, 6 in the decimal system. Our blackboards would not be big enough to figure sums using the binary method, but the electronic computer can recognize and manipulate long strings of zeroes and ones faster than man can even imagine. Since there are only two digits the operation can be performed in just two states of a circuit—on and off.

Whereas digital machines "count," analog computers "measure," meaning that they evaluate by comparison, or analogy. They consist of a true-or-false system, being a sort of mechanical decision-maker. A crude illustration of their differences might be between a machine that tells you exactly how many people are on a bus ahead of you, and a machine that says "That bus is too full for me to take my cello on." The analog computer uses current strengths that are varied according to the questions being considered. Their precision does not compare with that of the digital computer, but they are able to supply quick answers to a whole series of related questions.

All computers, digital and analog, have five basic units. The first is the *input unit*, where known data is fed to punched or magnetic tape. The second is the *arithmetic unit*, which contains logical circuits that actually carry out

Defying our sense of size, the thimble opposite contains some fifty thousand transistors, tiny chips of crystal that have become the minute workhorses of contemporary electronics. Introduced during the 1940's by the Bell Telephone Laboratories, the tiny transistor can actually perform all the functions of the familiar radio tube, and do them even better. It has been the transistor and the many other miniaturized devices that have made possible the exploration of space, since spaceships rely on complex instruments that must be relatively light. Below is a photograph of a tsetse fly, carrier of sleeping sickness, enlarged sixty times, another example of how machines can alter our concept of size. It is true but almost incomprehensible to realize that a molecule can be enlarged up to two hundred thousand times its original size.

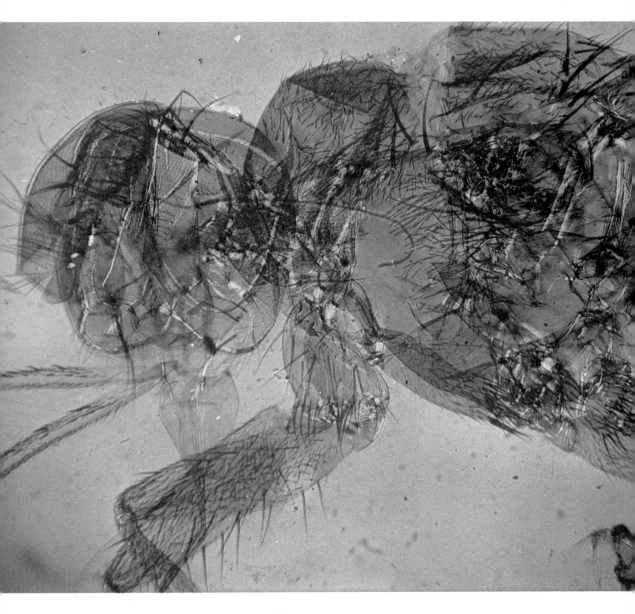

the computations; the third is the *memory* or *storage unit*, which holds and records intermediate data, and transfers them according to the directions given the machine. The fourth is the *control unit*, which programs and integrates the entire process; the last is the *output unit*, where the final solutions are expressed.

Many scientists complained when the computer was first described as an "electric brain." But today, certainly, the word "computer" is an understatement. It is not just a calculating machine; it has in many respects taken over. It manages faster and better the memory, the logical evaluation, and the external-control functions of the brain. It "learns" by experience and by correcting the human errors fed into it. This experience is then transferred to the next generation of computers, computers devised in part by their predecessors. The late John von Neumann of the Institute of Advanced Study early predicted that such machines would someday have enough parts and a sufficiently complicated structure to be self-reproducing. Some computer experts look forward to the day when their machines will actually be able to invent. Others disagree, insisting that a computer can know only what man has supplied it. True, they may be capable of choosing between available facts, but they remain completely unable to render value judgments. Regardless of these arguments it can not be denied that computers were a necessary precedent to the Space Age—certainly the electronic advances, the miniaturization of components, and the calculations vital to the design, launching, and orbit determination of space-

craft would not have been possible without the computer in its pristine form.

Space exploration actually began in 1957 with the beginning of an International Geophysical Year. Scientists of sixty-six nations were to co-operate to study planet earth and its envelope, and the cosmic forces impinging upon it. The program called not only for rocket probes to carry instruments for instant measurements, but also orbiting satellites that would carry out surveys of the earth and of cosmic rays from space. The Russians and Americans began a race in trying to launch these satellites, and on October 4, 1957, Sputnik I went into orbit, preceding by several months the first earth satellite of the United States, Explorer I.

The Russian satellite journeyed around the earth in an elliptical orbit, its distance from the earth's surface varying from 156 to 560 miles. It carried few scientific instruments, except for a mechanism that could record any meteoritic interference. It also included a radio transmitter and batteries that emitted back to the world its famous "beep."

The greatest difficulty in sending such a body into orbit was in overcoming the earth's force of gravity. A multi-stage rocket using enormous amounts of fuel had to be used to deliver the last stage of the rocket to its destination. To be finally placed in orbit the rocket demanded that equal and opposite forces act upon it. In other words, the force of the earth's gravity had to be exactly countered by the force of the rocket's engines. On each successive revolution around the globe, the satellite lost

Overleaf: the receiver built for the Telstar communications satellite at Andover, Maine. It receives waves "bounced" from a satellite that circles the globe every twenty-four hours, thus remaining stationary at a point above the Atlantic. Presently the antenna is fixed on Early Bird. With live global television the world has shrunk drastically, even for the most sedentary.

energy, thus slowly giving in to the earth's pull, and after three months its energy supply was weakened to the point where the rocket slipped into a denser atmosphere and burned up by friction with the air.

The Russian success, plus the so-called missile gap, led to an intensification of United States' rocket development and to Soviet counter-intensification. Ten years later the two crash programs were costing each of the competing countries billions of dollars a year. Space engineering had become a gigantic industry. The development of the means of propulsion—rocket motors—was important, but even more significant was its effect on the electronics industry. Although the spectacular object was to send people into orbit, or land them on the moon, the program was essentially the extension of human senses beyond the earth's limits. This meant telemetering devices reaching out to other planets in the solar system, and a mobilizing of scientists and technologists, blessed with lavish appropriations.

The impact of space research on the evolution of the machine, however, apart from the engineering achievement of breaking down the gravitational fences of the planet, caused an irreversible acceleration in the momentum of change. A new generation grew up with the rocket. It took this change entirely for granted. No youngster was overly shocked when astronaut Ed White stepped out of a space capsule traveling at 17,500 miles per hour. Speed of that order was just what you expected engineers to produce. And with radioed reports from Venus, or photographs from the surface

of the moon, distance had all but disappeared.

Instrumentation and the powering of those instruments demanded greater and greater ingenuity and miniaturization. Television was no longer something used merely for entertainment. It had become, as Norbert Wiener had predicted in 1940, a vital component of engineering, and its scanning techniques became an attribute of the computer as well as a built-in part of automation. The surface of a planet millions of miles away was scanned by the pulse-triggered automation in the capsule, and the visual information was sent back in the form of numbers, which computers would then convert into a recognizable photograph.

From World War II to the present, technology has evolved to a level where man now has, through his machines, the ability to create nearly anything he so desires. Time and distance are on the verge of extinction, and the widespread use of computers and the steady growth of automation reflect a technological know-how that scientists are only commencing to view in terms of social consequence. To help man understand and control the enormous effects and interrelationships of technological advances, a new science has evolved. It is called "cybernetics," deriving from a Greek word meaning helmsman, or one who steers a ship. In essence, cybernetics is involved with control and communication, whether in a machine or animate object. It represents an attempt to coordinate and communicate all existing scientific knowledge. The Lunar Society of the eighteenth century might be described as an early microcosm of cybernetic thinking.

The bow and arrow etherealized,
the laser, below, is a device
whose arrow is light itself,
but light more intense than any
ever known before. It emits
waves of a single length and
width moving in parallel lines,
making it possible to focus
great amounts of energy onto
extremely small areas. At
right is Edward White
seen taking man's first walk
in space while tied, like
nearly all of mankind, to
the ubiquitous machine.

Cybernetics, of which automation, in machine terminology, is but one expression, is the supreme example of the miscegenation of the sciences—mathematics, physics, chemistry, biology, sociology and anthropology—because it involves the systematic re-examination of all systems that respond through communication. In fact, one might complain that "communication" has become, over the last few years, an overworked term, encompassing everything from the computer selecting the right number to the community electing the wrong government. But more importantly it embodies an attempt to utilize and direct all scientific knowledge to man's advantage. In many respects cybernetics is an outgrowth of fear, fear that machines may one day be more dehumanizing and destructive than helpful.

But in having reservations about the future hegemony of a computerized machine that can marshal, control, operate, supply, and dispatch the products of automated plants, one is mainly expressing doubts about the way we have become infatuated by the machines we have created, and by the way we have become hypnotized by the mechanical genii thus released from the bottle of human creativeness.

Moreover, apart from the unresolved military and political consequences of the cataclysmic nuclear bomb, we have given the experts the freedom to turn the biosphere, the living space of our world, into a laboratory without walls, so that they could experiment with bigger and bigger bombs. Wisely, some have yelled "Stop!" to the radioactive fallout that has been poisoning, with man-made radioactive elements, the atmosphere, the soil, the plants, and people. For peaceful uses our safeguards have been elaborate, and maybe even excessively cautious, but it is, nevertheless, an awesome thought that burying the live atoms, the waste of atom factories, has cost one country, the United States, in the past twenty years, far, far more than it cost to bury all the pyramid kings of ancient Egypt.

We shudder at (mainly when we are affected personally) the death toll from automobile accidents. We see our cities becoming choked with traffic jams as each of us insists on having our own machine. We are blinded with smogs of gasoline and diesel fumes. Our chimneys have belched out so much carbon from fossil-fuels that it has upset the equilibrium by which nature holds the earth's carbon in balance. Changes in our climate have been the result. The industrialization that has come from all those wonderful machines has polluted our water supplies to an ominous extent and, because machines are more thirsty than people, has preempted the world's water supplies.

Machines are marvelous. Human ingenuity in creating them is the highest expression of toolmaking man. When, however, we contemplate the remarkable story of the evolution of the machine, with its liberation of men (at least in the highly advanced countries) from drudgery, we might, in making an inventory of our achievements, also make a prospectus of our purposes. We might be reminded that the use of all our wondrous contrivances must, in the last analysis, be determined by something no machine has yet supplied: wisdom.

In an historic photograph taken by Lunar Orbiter I, a crescent-shaped earth hangs in black space 232,000 miles in the distance. In the foreground is the surface of the moon. Whether man will, as he expects, cross that great divide within this decade will depend on the continuing evolution of the machine, just as the future quality of human life back on earth will depend on his ability to understand that evolution and to direct it wisely.

CHRONOLOGY

Palaeolithic Age. *Use of the wedge, lever, and inclined plane; hand-ax and other flint and stone implements used in hunting and food gathering.*

20,000 B.C. *Spear, knife, bow and arrow used in hunting; awl and bone needle used for sewing crude skin clothing.*

9000 B.C. *Elaboration of fishing equipment; use of the stone adz and chisel.*

3500 B.C. *Wheel and axle used for transport; first copper tools; hoe and sickle used in cultivation; spindle and loom used for textiles; first written records in cuneiform.*

3000 B.C. *Pottery wheel first used; beginning of hieroglyphics.*

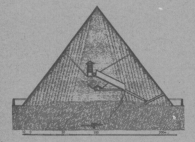

2500 B.C. *Construction of the Great Pyramid; use of seafaring sailing ships.*

2000 B.C. *First bronze implements; use of small plow.*

1500 B.C. *First evidence of the pulley; knowledge of glassmaking.*

1000 B.C. *Development of iron implements and strong swords.*

500 B.C. *Common use of the lathe for wood turning.*

400 B.C. *Invention of the catapult by the Greeks.*

270 B.C. *Ktesibios invents the force pump and the water clock; founds the science of hydraulics.*

250 B.C. *Archimedes devises a water snail and endless screw.*

60 A.D. *Hero of Alexandria records a number of important inventions including the aeolipile (a toy steam turbine) and the screw press. Use of the water mill spreads throughout Italy.*

600 *Persia develops the horizontal windmill.*

800 *Emergence of the modern horse harness increases horse-power by four to five times.*

1100 *Papermaking industry develops in southern Europe.*

1185 *Invention of the horizontal-axle windmill in North Sea region.*

1190 *The magnetic compass reaches Europe from the East.*

1300 *Development of the spinning wheel in Europe.*

1325 *Invention of the cannon and the first use of gunpowder.*

1440 *Johann Gutenberg invents the printing press in Germany.*

1450 *Introduction of the hand gun, replacing the cross bow as man's most effective weapon.*

1452-1519 *Leonardo da Vinci designs a gig mill and spring-driven clock; foresees such inventions as the flying machine, the tank, the spinning machine, and the paddle-wheel boat.*

1569 *Jacques Besson develops the screw-cutting lathe.*

1581 *Principle of the pendulum discovered by Galileo.*

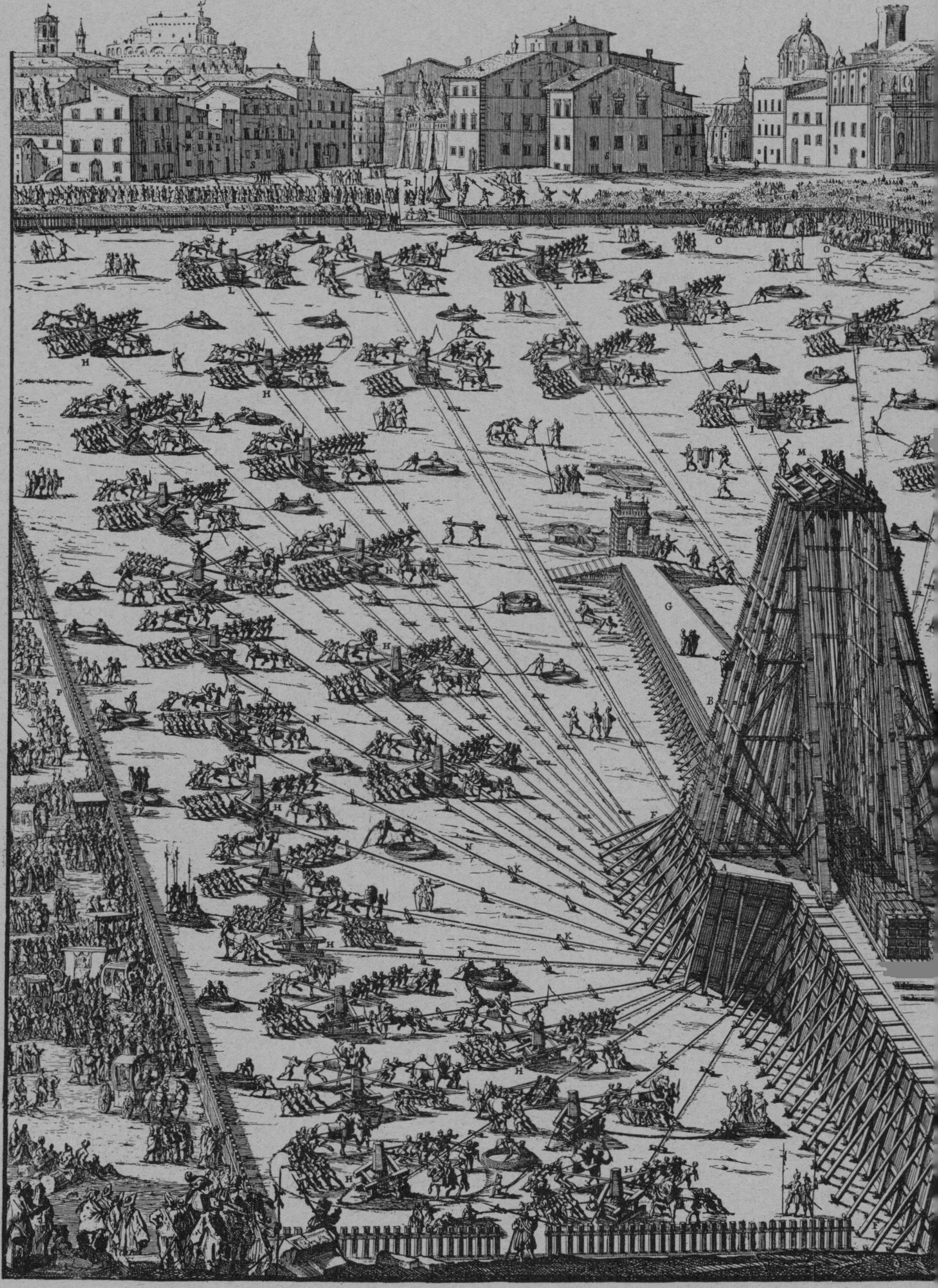

Eques Carolus Fontana Delineavit.   Aloys. Specchus Sculp.

1586 *Raising of an Egyptian obelisk in Rome employs the same technological principles used by Greeks centuries before.*

1609 *Galileo builds the first modern telescope.*

1642 *Blaise Pascal invents the first calculating machine.*

1643 *Evangelista Torricelli invents the barometer to demonstrate the existence of atmospheric pressure.*

1650-1654 *Otto von Guericke constructs the first air pump, thereby demonstrating the power of the vacuum.*

1660 *Von Guericke invents a frictional electrical device—the first machine to generate electricity.*

1673 *Christian Huygens develops the pendulum clock.*

1680 *Huygens introduces the principle of internal combustion.*

1690 *Denis Papin designs a primitive steam engine.*

1698 *Thomas Savery constructs the first useful steam engine.*

1712 *Thomas Newcomen constructs an improved model of the steam engine.*

1746 *Pieter van Musschenbrock constructs the first electrical condenser—the Leyden jar.*

1752

1752 *Benjamin Franklin demonstrates the concept of "positive" and "negative" electricity with his famous kite-and-key experiment.*

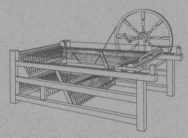

1764 *James Hargreaves invents the spinning jenny.*

1765-1785 *James Watt perfects the steam engine, introducing the separate condenser, double-action rotary feature, and speed governor.*

1769-1775 *Richard Arkwright develops the water frame for carding, roving, and spinning.*

1770 *Nicolas Cugnot constructs the first steam-driven land vehicle.*

1774 *John Wilkinson designs a precision cylinder-boring mill.*

1779 *Samuel Crompton invents the spinning mule, combining elements of the jenny and water frame.*

1784 *Scotsman Andrew Meikle invents the threshing machine.*

1785 *Edmund Cartwright builds the first successful power loom.*

1787 *John Fitch builds and demonstrates a thirty-foot steamboat on the Delaware River.*

1792 *William Murdock shows the commercial possibilities of illumination by coal gas.*

1793 *Eli Whitney invents the cotton gin.*

1798 *Nicolas-Louis Robert invents a machine for producing paper in continuous lengths.*

1800 *Alessandro Volta announces his invention of the electric battery.*

1801 *J. M. Jacquard invents a silk loom for mass production.*

1803 *John Dalton advances his theory of the atomic composition of all matter.*

1804 *Richard Trevithick constructs the first rail locomotive.*

1804 *George Cayley begins experimentation with gliders.*

1807 *Robert Fulton's steamboat* Clermont *makes a successful voyage up the Hudson between New York City and Albany.*

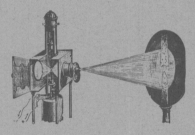

1809-1810 *Humphry Davy invents the carbon arc lamp.*

1812 *Friedrich König's cylinder press adopted by the London* Times.

1820 *Hans Christian Oersted discovers the relationship between electricity and magnetism.*

1822 *Charles Babbage develops a complex calculating machine, forerunner of the modern computer.*

1825 *George Stephenson builds the world's first modern railway between Stockton and Darlington in northern England.*

1825 *Oersted produces small amounts of aluminum by a process of chemical reduction.*

1826 *Joseph Niepce makes first successful photograph.*

1830 *Joseph Henry constructs a primitive electric motor.*

1831 Michael Faraday advances the principle of electromagnetic induction and constructs an experimental electric generator.

1834 Cyrus McCormick patents the first successful reaper.

1834 M. H. Jacobi develops a battery-powered electric motor.

1835 Samuel Colt patents the revolver, or "six-shooter."

1835 Henry invents the electrical relay, forerunner of the telegraph.

1837 Cooke and Wheatstone patent an electric telegraph.

1837 John Deere introduces the first steel plow.

1838 Introduction of the screw propeller and the beginning of transatlantic steamers.

1839 Charles Goodyear discovers the process of vulcanizing rubber.

1844 Samuel F. B. Morse builds the first practical telegraph.

1846 Richard M. Hoe develops the rotary printing press.

1846 Elias Howe invents the modern sewing machine.

1847 Joseph Swan begins experimentation with incandescent filament lamps.

1851 F.S. Archer introduces the wet collodion process for developing photographic film.

1851 Isaac Singer patents his sewing machine.

1851 Submarine telegraph cable laid across the English Channel.

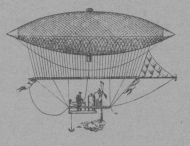

1852 Henri Giffard builds the first practical steam-propelled dirigible balloon.

1856 Henry Bessemer develops the blast furnace for steelmaking.

1856-1863 Siemens-Martin process of open-hearth steelmaking is introduced.

1859 First oil well drilled at Titusville, Pennsylvania.

1860 Étienne Lenoir constructs the first successful gas engine.

1860 Oliver Winchester introduces the repeating rifle.

1860 Philipp Reis constructs an experimental telephone.

1862 Beau de Rochas develops the four-stroke cycle for internal combustion engines.

1862 Richard J. Gatling invents the machine gun.

1866 Alfred Nobel invents the explosive known as dynamite.

1866 Successful laying of the transatlantic cable.

1868 George Westinghouse introduces the air brake.

1869 Completion of the first transcontinental railway in America.

1869 I. W. McGaffey patents a suction-type vacuum sweeper.

1870 John W. Hyatt develops the first celluloid plastic.

1871 Z. T. Gramme designs a ring-dynamo for generating a continuous flow of electricity.

1873 C. L. Sholes introduces the typewriter in America.

1873 Willoughby Smith discovers the photoconductive effect.

The lonely experiments of young Elias Howe led to

. . . a wonderous lock-stitch sewing machine, then

. . . to London, where his genius went unnoticed.

He borrowed money for his passage back home . . .

and having successfully sued all his competitors

. . . at long last he found himself a very rich man.

A VICTORIAN VERSION OF AN INVENTOR'S TRIALS AND TRIUMPH

1875 *William Crookes develops the cathode-ray tube.*

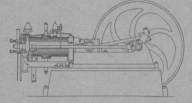

1876 *Nikolaus Otto constructs a successful gas engine, the prototype of the modern car engine.*

1876 *Alexander Graham Bell patents the telephone.*

1877 *Thomas A. Edison invents the phonograph.*

1879 *Edison perfects the incandescent electric lamp.*

1882 *Edison establishes the first large-scale electric power system in New York City.*

1884 *Edison patents but dismisses the "Edison effect."*

1884 *Charles Parsons patents the compound steam turbine.*

1884 *First long distance telephone transmission established between Boston and New York.*

1885 *Ottmar Mergenthaler invents the linotype machine.*

1885 *Hungarian inventors Zipernowsky, Beri, and Blathy patent the first practical electrical transformer.*

1885-1887 *Karl Benz and Gottlieb Daimler construct the first petrol-engine automobiles.*

1886 *Charles Hall and Toussaint Héroult independently discover the process of direct electrolysis of alumina dissolved in cryolite.*

1887 *Tolbert Lanston patents the monotype machine.*

1887 *Heinrich Hertz discovers the photoelectric effect.*

1887 *Frank L. Sprague installs the first extensive electric streetcar system in Richmond, Virginia.*

1887 *Emile Berliner invents the "gramophone" and later produces a marketable disk-record.*

1888 *Nikola Tesla invents the alternating-current motor.*

1888 *J. B. Dunlop introduces the pneumatic rubber tire.*

1888 *William Burroughs produces the first commercially successful adding machines.*

1888 *Hannibal Goodwin introduces the use of celluloid film in photography.*

1892 *Rudolf Diesel patents the Diesel engine.*

1893 *Edison demonstrates his "kinetoscope," an early motion picture projector.*

1895 *Guglielmo Marconi begins experimentation with wireless telegraphy.*

1895 *Wilhelm Röntgen discovers X-rays, or Röntgen rays.*

1895 *Installation of the Niagara Falls hydroelectric power plant.*

1896 *Henri Becquerel discovers the phenomenon of radioactivity.*

1898 *Valdemar Poulsen invents the "telegraphone," a kind of early tape recorder.*

1898 *Marie and Pierre Curie isolate two new radioactive elements, "polonium" and "radium."*

1900 *Max Planck announces his quantum theory.*

1901 *Marconi sends the first wireless signal across the Atlantic.*

1902 *Valdemar Poulsen invents the arc transmitter.*

1903 *Orville and Wilbur Wright make the first successful powered-airplane flight.*

1904 *John Ambrose Fleming patents the thermionic valve.*

In the 1890's Englishman
Hiram Maxim constructed
this eight thousand-pound
"multiplane." It was based on
the principle of the kite
and depended chiefly on
sheer power to give it lift.
During a test run along a
double track intended to fix
the contraption firmly to the
ground, its mighty engine
generated such power that the
plane uprooted the tracks and
nearly took off. Fortunately,
Maxim cut the power and
avoided almost certain death.

1905 Albert Einstein announces his special theory of relativity.

1906 Reginald Fessenden transmits the first modulated radio-wave broadcast.

1907 Leo H. Baekeland develops the first synthetic plastic.

1907 Lee De Forest invents the three-electrode (triode) vacuum tube, important in the future development of the radio.

1908 Henry Ford introduces the assembly line for mass production of his "Model T" automobile.

1908 Hans Geiger and Ernest Rutherford invent the Geiger counter, a device for detecting subatomic particles.

1913 René Lorin conceives the idea of jet propulsion.

1914 Ernest Rutherford discovers the proton.

1919 Rutherford splits the atom, thus achieving the first atomic transmutation.

1920 Opening of the first commercial radio station in Pittsburgh, Pennsylvania.

1922 Francis Jenkins invents the telephoto for transmitting photographs over telephone wires.

1925 Introduction of the first successful sound-motion pictures.

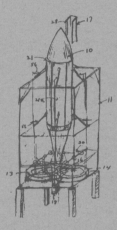

1926 Robert Goddard launches the first liquid-fuel rocket.

1927 Charles Lindbergh makes a transatlantic flight from New York to Paris.

1927 Establishment of the first transatlantic telephone service.

1928 Alexander Fleming discovers penicillin.

1929 Vladimir Zworykin designs a practical television system with his "iconoscope" (pickup tube) and "kinescope" (receiving tube).

1930 Ernest Lawrence conceives the cyclotron, or atom-smasher.

1930 Wallace Carothers produces the first synthetic fiber.

1931 Harold Urey discovers deuterium, principle power source for the hydrogen bomb.

1932 *James Chadwick proves the existence of the neutron, and Carl D. Anderson discovers the positive electron, or positron.*

1934 *Frederic and Irene Joliot-Curie produce the first artificial radioactive isotope.*

1935 *Robert Watson-Watt develops radar for detection of airplanes by radio-wave reflection.*

1937 *Frank Whittle constructs the first successful jet engine.*

1939 *Germany introduces the first turbojet plane, He-178.*

1942 *Establishment of the Manhattan Project for the development of the atomic bomb.*

1942 *Enrico Fermi constructs the first nuclear reactor.*

1942 *Wernher von Braun develops the long-range V-2 rocket.*

1944 *IBM and Harvard develop the Mark I computer.*

1945 *U.S. test-explodes the first atomic bomb at Alamogordo, New Mexico.*

1946 *Construction of the first large electronic computer (ENIAC) is completed at the University of Pennsylvania.*

1947 *An American Bell X-1 is the first plane to break the sound barrier.*

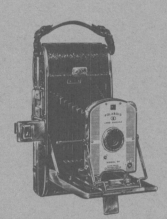

1947 *Edwin H. Land invents the Polaroid Land Camera.*

1948 *Shockley, Bardeen, and Brattain invent the transistor.*

1951 *First use of atomic power for electric lighting.*

1952 *U.S. test-explodes the first hydrogen bomb.*

1953 *Donald Glaser invents the liquid hydrogen "bubble chamber" for photographing atomic particles.*

1954 *The first solar battery developed by two U.S. companies.*

1954 *Charles Townes invents the maser (molecular amplification by stimulated emission of radiation).*

1956 *Britain constructs a system of atomic generating stations.*

1957 *Russia launches the first artificial space satellite, Sputnik I.*

1957 *U.S. installs a full-scale atomic power station on the Ohio River.*

1958 *Charles Townes and A. L. Schawlow invent the laser (light amplification by stimulated emission of radiation).*

1958 *James Van Allen discovers the Van Allen high-energy radiation belt in outer space.*

1958 *First atomic-powered submarine, U.S.S. Nautilus, makes undersea crossing of the North Pole.*

1958 *First U.S. satellite, Explorer I, orbits the earth.*

1959 *Russia's Luna II, the first satellite to reach the moon, makes a crash landing.*

1961 *Yuri Gagarin makes first manned orbital space flight in Russian spacecraft Vostok I.*

1962 *U.S. satellite Telstar provides first direct telephone and television communication between U.S. and Europe.*

1965 *Aleksei Leonov of Russia is first man to walk in space.*

1966 *Russia's Luna IX makes first soft landing on the moon; transmits television photos of the lunar surface.*

1967 *U.S. launches Saturn 5, the largest, most powerful rocket ever sent into space.*

"YES, BUT WILL IT FLY?"

Since the establishment of the U.S. patent system in 1790, the federal government has officially acknowledged a staggering number of gadgets and inventions (3,343,175 as of September, 1967). Many have contributed substantially to the advance of technology (and of mankind), while others, like those illustrated in this special portfolio, demonstrate, intentionally or otherwise, a lighter side of what has been called Yankee ingenuity. Among the nation's more colorful patents is the "Saluting Device," below, which enabled a proper Victorian gentleman to tip his hat without lifting a finger.

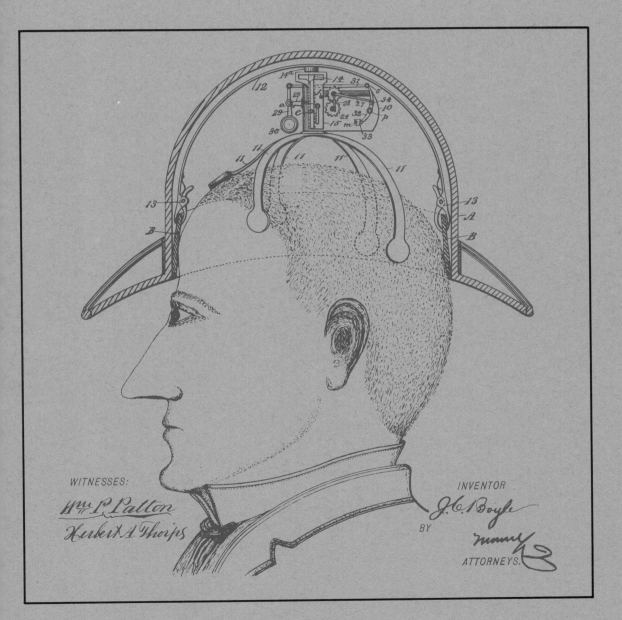

WITNESSES:

Wm P. Patton

Herbert A. Thorps

INVENTOR

J. C. Boyle

BY

[signature]

ATTORNEYS.

COMMUTER'S AIDE *might be slung like a portable hammock between train seats as shown. Thus suspended, the weary gentleman was presumably at perfect ease, though how his legs might feel at the end of his trip was perhaps another matter.*

BATHING DEVICE *for producing artificial waves was patented in 1900. Equipped with a rocking board for easy wave-making and a curved headrest for comfort, its failure to create a market may have been due to problems inherent in the head-down position.*

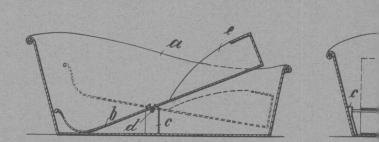

GNAT-GAT, *intended for the extermination of all kinds of insects, was also intended as a plaything for youngsters. The swatting projectile was propelled by a tightly coiled spring as shown. It could accommodate itself to various surfaces without damaging them. At close range it must have dealt instant over-kill.*

NOISELESS ALARMS, *a device patented by Mr. Charles W. Waller in 1921, employed a stethoscopic arrangement that was designed to provide direct communication between sleeper and "a clock of ordinary construction" without disturbing the sleep of one's neighbor. It might have been wise to check volume of "ordinary alarm" before retiring. This admirable invention was, no doubt, inspired by Mrs. Waller.*

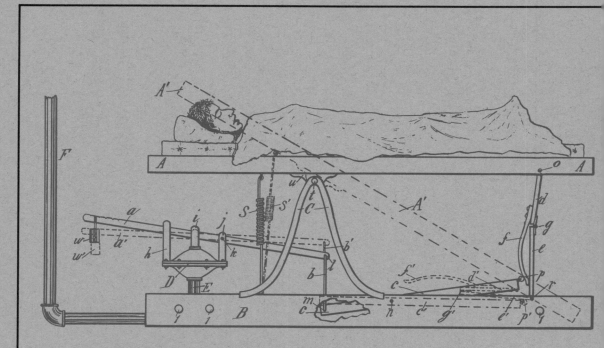

ALARM-BED *was not recommended as a substitute for a clock, but was intended for use in "hot-houses and conservatories." It was so arranged that "should the steam in the heating pipes fall below a certain pressure it will tilt the bed to awaken the sleeper having charge of the heating plant."*

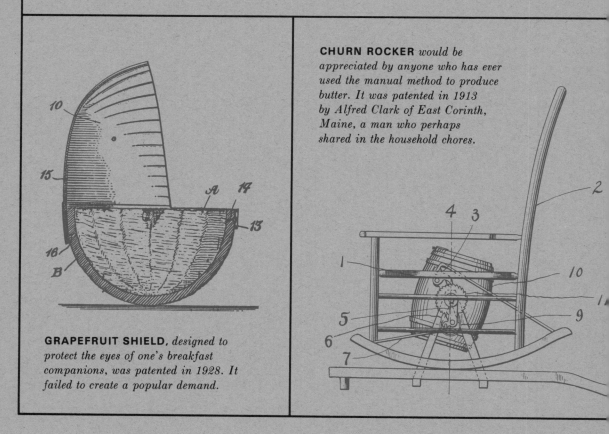

CHURN ROCKER *would be appreciated by anyone who has ever used the manual method to produce butter. It was patented in 1913 by Alfred Clark of East Corinth, Maine, a man who perhaps shared in the household chores.*

GRAPEFRUIT SHIELD, *designed to protect the eyes of one's breakfast companions, was patented in 1928. It failed to create a popular demand.*

HIGH-STEPPING CLEANER *was patented in 1912 as an improvement on the hand-bellows vacuum of the day. It could be operated by the simple process of walking. Each foot-bellows had an adjustable spring to suit the weight of the operator and an adaptable foot piece to fit any boot. While its inventor claimed that "no novel or unusual muscular movements are involved by the operation," one can only speculate as to its effects on the housewife's stride and posture.*

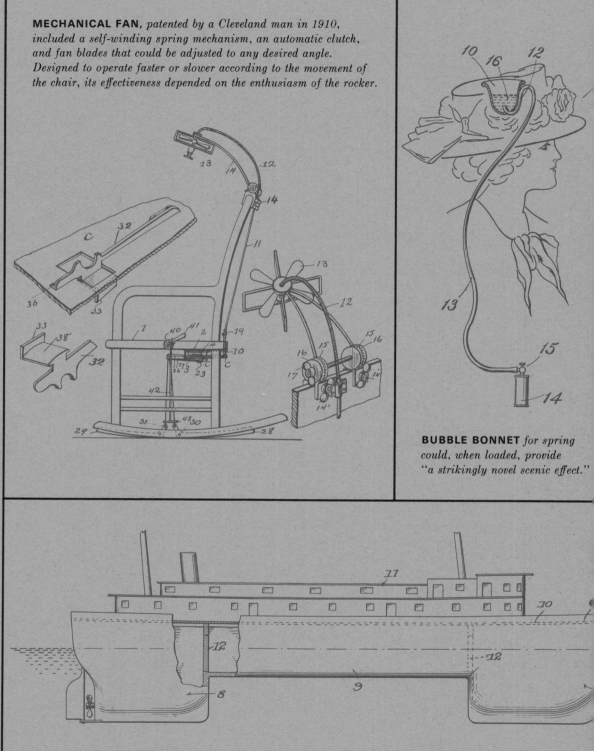

MECHANICAL FAN, *patented by a Cleveland man in 1910, included a self-winding spring mechanism, an automatic clutch, and fan blades that could be adjusted to any desired angle. Designed to operate faster or slower according to the movement of the chair, its effectiveness depended on the enthusiasm of the rocker.*

BUBBLE BONNET *for spring could, when loaded, provide "a strikingly novel scenic effect."*

SUB-SAFE SHIP, *said to be "substantially immune from damage from torpedo attacks," was the inspiration of a Wisconsin man in 1919. Since torpedos generally attack midship to destroy the power plant, the latter was moved fore and aft to foil the enemy.*

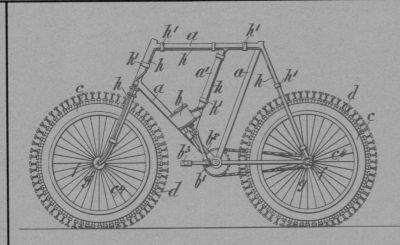

SELF-PROPELLING *bicycle was ingeniously equipped with an air motor and special wheels with piston pumps radiating from their periphery. As the wheels revolved, the weight of the rider forced air into the tires, then through the hollow spokes to the axles, and then through narrow tubes or pipes to the motor.*

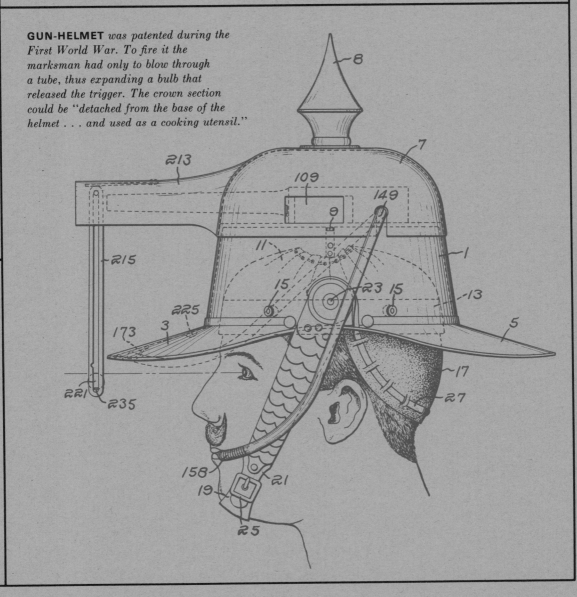

GUN-HELMET *was patented during the First World War. To fire it the marksman had only to blow through a tube, thus expanding a bulb that released the trigger. The crown section could be "detached from the base of the helmet . . . and used as a cooking utensil."*

MAKERS
OF THE
MODERN
WORLD

ARKWRIGHT, *Richard,*
English inventor (1732-1792)

Arkwright was the youngest of
thirteen children born to a poor
laborer. Trained as a barber, he
developed a new process for
dyeing hair and entered the
wigmaking business. When wigs
fell to disuse Arkwright undertook
the construction of a spinning
machine. By 1775 he had
developed mills in which the entire

process of manufacturing yarn
was carried out by one machine.
As a skilled businessman he
organized large-scale production
in his factories and divided labor
into separate groups. So
successful were Arkwright's
machines in replacing manual
labor that rioters protesting the
introduction of machinery in
Lancashire forced his exile to
Nottingham. Despite such
setbacks his methods triumphed,
and he was rewarded with
knighthood in 1786.

BELL, *Alexander Graham,*
Scottish-American inventor (1847-
1922)

Although his fame rests chiefly
on the invention of the telephone,
Bell's consuming interest was in
helping the deaf. As a young man
he worked closely with his father,
a professor of elocution and vocal
physiology in London. In 1871
Bell came to Boston, began a
training program for teachers of
the deaf, and later became a
professor of vocal physiology at

Boston University. Through his
studies of resonance pitches he
became interested in the
mechanical reproduction of the
human voice, and in 1874 he
conceived the idea of the telephone.
Two years later he transmitted the
first intelligible sentence over wires
and patented his invention. In
1877 he organized the Bell
Telephone Company and traveled
to France and England to
introduce the telephone there.
Devoting his later years to
aviation research, he invented the
tetrahedral kite and founded the
Aerial Experiment Association.
He was also one of the early
presidents of the National
Geographic Society. Bell lived to
see his telephone spread from
coast to coast, and in 1915 he
spoke to his assistant Thomas
A. Watson over the first
transcontinental wire.

BESSEMER, *Henry, English*
inventor (1813-1898)

The "Bessemer process," which
revolutionized the steelmaking
industry, had its beginnings in the
Crimean War of the early 1850's.
Experimenting with new
weapons for use against Britain's
enemy, Russia, Bessemer
designed a rotating artillery shell
of long range and great
accuracy. Since the cast-iron
cannons of the day were not strong
enough to withstand the greater
pressures necessary to fire them
Bessemer set about to create
a stronger material. What

he needed was steel, and Bessemer's answer was the blast-furnace, in which iron could be converted into steel without the use of fuel. In 1860 he established his own steelworks and began to amass a fortune with his new and cheap steel process. Toward the end of his life Bessemer devoted himself to improvements in steamers, solar furnaces, and telescopes. He patented over one hundred inventions. He was made a fellow of the Royal Society, was knighted in 1879, and helped found the British Iron and Steel Institute in 1873.

DAVY, Humphry, English chemist (1778-1829)

Apprenticed to an apothecary, Davy became actively interested in chemistry after reading Lavoisier's chemistry textbook in 1797. He began experimenting with the anaesthetic properties of gases and soon discovered nitrous oxide. In 1801 he was made a professor at the Royal Institution in London, where he began to experiment with the effect of electricity on certain metallic compounds. In 1807 he ran an electric current through a molten potash solution and isolated the metal potassium. Applying his process of electrolysis to soda, he isolated sodium, and the next year he isolated barium, strontium, calcium, and magnesium. In 1810 he invented the carbon arc lamp, the first application of electricity for illumination. In 1818 he was made a baronet and two years later was elected president of the Royal Society.

De FOREST, Lee, American inventor and radio engineer (1873-1961)

A pioneer in the development of radio, De Forest patented more than three hundred inventions in the field of wireless communications. A graduate of Yale University (where he was

voted the "ugliest and freshest man of his class"), De Forest became interested in wireless telegraphy in the early 1900's and devised an alternating current transmitter used as a method of news reporting during the Russo-Japanese War. In 1907 he patented his most important invention, the triode—a three electrode vacuum tube that is the basis of modern radio. In 1910 he used it to broadcast the voice of Enrico Caruso, and by 1916 he was broadcasting news from

his own radio station. De Forest also invented the glow-light method of recording sound films, and in 1923 demonstrated one of the earliest sound motion pictures.

DIESEL, Rudolf, German engineer (1858-1913)

While still a college student Rudolf Diesel began to experiment with the principles of internal combustion. In 1892 he constructed his first engine, which upon starting for the first time exploded and nearly killed him. By 1897 its errors were remedied and the first successful Diesel engine was installed in St. Louis one year later. The Diesel provided a cheap and efficient power source for electricity, plants, factories, mines, and heavy transport vehicles such as ships and locomotives. Despite the importance of his invention, Diesel never accrued a fortune.

His death in 1913 is marked by mystery. He disappeared from a steamer while crossing the English Channel (it has been presumed that he fell overboard). His papers have also oddly disappeared.

EDISON, Thomas A., American inventor (1847-1931)

Born in the small Ohio town of Milan, young Edison received no more than three months of formal education. Openly rebellious against all authority, he was taken out of school and tutored by his mother. An avid reader, he became interested in chemistry and set up his own laboratory at the age of ten. At sixteen he began experimenting with telegraphy, and in 1868 he patented his first invention, an electrical vote recorder. Eight years later he set up a research laboratory in Menlo Park, New Jersey, and before his death he had patented more than a thousand inventions, including a carbon telephone transmitter, a system of telegraphic trans-mission, a stock-ticker, the mimeograph, the megaphone, the phonograph, the incandescent light, the kinetoscope, and various railroad signaling devices. He also improved upon the motion picture and the alkali storage battery. Among American inventors he had no peer, and unlike many other giants of American science, Thomas Edison became in his own lifetime one of the nations great folk heroes. With Edison the age of the "inventor at large" died and the age of the specialist began.

FARADAY, Michael, *English physicist and chemist (1791-1867)*

The son of a poor blacksmith, Faraday educated himself with the material that passed through his hands where he worked as a bookbinder. In 1812 he came to the attention of Humphry Davy, whose lectures he had been attending at the Royal Institution, and the following year he became Davy's assistant. A brilliant scientist, he soon outstripped his master. He was the first to produce laboratory temperatures below 0° F. and the first to discover benzene. In 1832 he announced what are known as Faraday's laws of electrolysis, introducing such terms as electrode, anode, and ionization. His greatest contribution, however, was in the field of electromagnetism. In 1831 he announced his discovery of electromagnetic induction and produced the first electric generator. Faraday's invention made possible the first cheap, large-scale production of electric current. Like his American counterpart, Joseph Henry, Faraday cared little for money or public acclaim. He was satisfied with a modest salary, and in 1824, when elected to the Royal Society, declined an offer of its presidency, as he later declined the honor of knighthood.

FORD, Henry *American industrialist (1863-1947)*

Born on a farm near Dearborn, Michigan, young Ford disliked farm work but showed an early passion for the workings of machines. At sixteen, with little formal education, he became a machinist's apprentice; by thirty he was chief engineer at the Edison works, an electric light company in Detroit. It was in his spare hours, however, that he fostered his first love. Working with his wife, in a shed behind his home, he built his first automobile—a two-cylinder, five-hundred pounder that he tested in 1893. In 1903 the tall, thin entrepreneur formed the Ford Motor Company and began building the Model T. His adaptation of the assembly line system revolutionized American industrial technique and inaugurated the era of mass production. By 1926 sales of Ford's "Tin Lizzie," as the Model T was affectionately called, totaled fifteen million. Toward the end of his life he established the Ford Foundation, the world's greatest philanthropic center.

GODDARD, Robert H. *American physicist (1882-1945)*

In 1935, after twenty-two years of experimentation, Robert Goddard launched a liquid-propellant rocket to a height of 6,240 feet at a spectacular speed of 527 miles per hour. A physics professor at Clark University, Goddard first came to public attention in 1919 when the Smithsonian Institution published a report in which he talked of sending a rocket to the moon. In 1926 he launched his first rocket, and three years later the Smithsonian sponsored him in a larger enterprise near Worcester, Massachusetts. But as a result of ensuing publicity the reticent Goddard set up an experimental station in New Mexico where he could work in seclusion. An exacting scientist, he was not satisfied even with his 1935 success. "The first few feet of the ascent," he wrote, "reminded me strongly of a fish swimming upwards." Before his death, however, Goddard had established the groundwork for the essential features of the modern rocket.

GOODYEAR, Charles, *American inventor (1800-1860)*

Goodyear was a selfless, ill-fated man whose inventive genius was rewarded with frustration and poverty. In 1821 he began a hardware business with his father that went bankrupt in 1830. Young Goodyear next turned his attention to an idea that had intrigued him for years—how to make rubber resist temperature extremes. For ten years—between frequent visits to debtor's prison—he worked on the problem with unsatisfactory results. Then, accidentally dropping a mixture of sulfur and rubber on a hot stove, he discovered the process of vulcanization. He perfected the process and patented it in 1844. But the method was easily imitated, and Goodyear became involved in a series of patent disputes. Although he finally won his case the prolonged litigation left him discouraged and

impoverished. His hard, flexible rubber eventually became standard for automobile tires, and his name lives on today as a manufacturing trademark.

GUERICKE, Otto von, German physicist (1602-1686)

A man of many interests and abilities, Guericke began as an engineer, served in the Thirty Years War, and in 1646 became

mayor of Magdeburg, the town of his birth. About that time, he became interested in a philosophical dispute over the possibility of a vacuum, the existence of which Aristotle had earlier denied. Von Guericke resolved to settle the question empirically, and in 1650 he invented the air pump to carry out his experiments. With it he was able to empty a vessel of air, and in 1654 he dramatically demonstrated the power of the vacuum. Evacuating two closely fitted hemispheres, he showed that two teams of eight horses could not pull them apart until air was permitted to enter, breaking the vacuum. He also devised the first electrical generating machine, a globe of sulphur on a crank-turned shaft. The friction of the hand held against the revolving ball generated static electricity. Invented in 1660, Von Guericke's machine led to a century of experimentation, culminating in the work of Benjamin Franklin.

HENRY, Joseph, American physicist (1797-1878)

Apprenticed to a watchmaker at the age of thirteen, Henry had little schooling and little opportunity for reading in his youth. His interest in science seems to have been sparked by a book on experimental philosophy that he happened upon while embarking on a theatrical career. He gave up the stage and began working his way through Albany Academy. Then in 1826 he became a professor of mathematics and started experimenting with electricity. In 1830 he produced the first primitive electric motor, and five years later constructed an electromagnetic relay system—in effect, the first electric telegraph. Henry is also credited with co-discovery of the principle of induction, although it was Faraday who first published the discovery, with Henry crediting him with priority. In 1846 Henry, by then a professor at Princeton University, became the first secretary of the Smithsonian Institution, and under his direction it became a vital center of research and a clearinghouse for the world's scientists. Strikingly handsome, known for his poise and determination, Henry was an inspired leader as well as the preeminent American scientist of his time.

KELVIN, William Thomson, Lord, Scottish physicist (1824-1907)

Lord Kelvin (born William Thomson) was an eccentric genius who sincerely believed that the average person could grasp the

most complex scientific facts if properly explained, because he himself had difficulty remembering the basic multiplication tables. As a professor at Glasgow University he was responsible for the invention of the mirror galvanometer, the dynamometer, the gyrostat, the quadrant electrometer, the siphon recorder, the curb transmitter, the tide predictor, and an improved mariner's compass. He was the first to define the absolute scale of temperature (the Kelvin scale), the first to estimate the age of the earth from solidification, and the first to design a vapour pressure thermometer to read from $100°$ to $500°C$. In 1866 he was knighted and in 1892 was named Baron Kelvin of Largs.

McCORMICK, Cyrus, American inventor (1809-1884)

In 1832 a group of disbelieving Virginia farmers watched Cyrus McCormick's "reaper" mow down a field of grain faster than they could have done it collectively. Soon the McCormick machine was replacing manual labor on farms throughout the country. McCormick was the son of a deeply religious farmer-inventor. Together they rebelled against the toil of hand-harvesting grain and began experimenting with labor-saving devices in their own blacksmith shop. In 1834, improving on his father's earlier machines, he patented the reaper, a year after Obed Hussey of Ohio had patented a similar device of his own invention. McCormick was forced into bitter competition when his patent rights expired in 1848, but his entrepreneurial skills nearly rivalled his inventiveness. By advertising, demonstrating, guaranteeing his products, and offering installment buying, McCormick remained the leader in the industry. Upon his death in 1884, his widow Nettie became the first woman to assume leadership of a major corporation.

MARCONI, *Guglielmo, Italian inventor (1874-1937)*

Born to wealth and aristocracy, Marconi enjoyed the private tutelage of some of Italy's best-known physicists. The idea of the wireless first struck him in 1894, after he read an article by Heinrich Hertz on electro-magnetic waves. Applying the results of Maxwell, Hertz, and others he constructed his first telegraph, and in 1896 journeyed to England to promote it. His successful experiments along England's coast made the handsome Italian a daily topic of local conversation, as well as a national hero in Italy. Marconi's crowning achievement came in 1901 when he sent the first radio signal across the Atlantic Ocean. The wireless remained for him the fascination and work of a lifetime, and in 1909 he was awarded the Nobel Prize in physics. Personally withdrawn and scornful of petty conversation, Marconi's natural reserve and high intelligence were sometimes misinterpreted as snobbery.

MORSE, *Samuel F.B., American artist and inventor (1791-1872)*

The son of a famous theologian, Jedediah Morse, and a graduate of Yale (1810), Morse achieved considerable fame as an artist and helped to found the National Academy of Design. In the 1830's, after a brief and unsuccessful fling at politics, he became interested in the study of electricity. With single-minded determination and the help of his friend Joseph Henry, Morse set about to construct a practical telegraph. After battling for patent rights and fighting for a government subsidy, he finally persuaded Congress to appropriate funds for a telegraph line from Washington to Baltimore. In 1844 he sent the first message over the forty-mile wire in the dot-dash signal of the Morse code. His invention won

him immediate acclaim. He was later instrumental in introducing the daguerreotype into the U.S.

OERSTED, *Hans Christian Danish physicist (1777-1851)*

A quiet, unassuming physics professor, Oersted made his greatest discovery during a classroom demonstration at the University of Copenhagen in 1819. Placing a compass near an electric-current wire with which he

was experimenting, he noticed that the wire caused the compass needle to waver and point at right angles to the direction of the current. The following year he announced his discovery of electromagnetism. Those who discredit Oersted's discovery because of its accidental nature fail to remember that it was left for Oersted to interpret the phenomenon. His discovery made possible the subsequent development of electricity, telegraphy, telephony, and the transmission of electric power. The electromagnetic unit of force, the oersted, is named in his honor.

PARSONS, *Charles, British engineer (1854-1931)*

The youngest son of famed astonomer Lord Rosse, Parsons chose to devote his talents to engineering. After studying at the University of Dublin, he concentrated on the use of steam power for high-velocity, rotary engines. In 1884 he developed the first practical steam turbine. By 1891 he had added a condenser, and three years later he patented an invention making his turbine applicable to ship propulsion. His engine was dramatically demonstrated in 1897 with the ship Turbinia, which cruised along at the then unbelievable speed of 35 knots, noiselessly and without vibration. Parsons continued to improve his turbine, and in 1911 he was knighted.

PASCAL, *Blaise, French mathematician and physicist (1623-1662)*

By the time he was sixteen Pascal had written a treatise on the geometry of conic sections that became the foundation for all contemporary inquiries into the subject. In 1643, at the age of nineteen, he invented a calculating machine—the forerunner of the modern cash register. Soon after, in conjunction with another French mathematician, Pierre de Fermat, he founded the theory of probability, establishing for the first time a mathematical basis for prediction. A master physicist, he founded the science of hydrodynamics and established the principle of the hydraulic press. Toward the end of his short life

Pascal came under the influence of an anti-Jesuit Catholic sect and devoted himself to meditation and religious writings, some of which inspired Voltaire. Chronically ill, ascetic, and suffering from insomnia, Pascal died at the age of thirty-nine.

PRIESTLEY, *Joseph, English chemist (1733-1804)*

A Unitarian minister from Fieldhead, Yorkshire, Priestley took up the study of science, and particularly electrical research, after meeting Benjamin Franklin in 1766. But a quirk of fate soon led him into chemistry. The young

minister had taken a pastorate near a brewery in Leeds, and his interest was sparked by a gas produced from the fermenting

grain. He discovered that it was carbon dioxide, a gas that when dissolved in water produced a refreshing drink now known as seltzer. Continuing his study of gases, Priestley isolated ammonia and hydrogen chloride; and in 1774 he made his most important scientific contribution: the discovery of oxygen. A political nonconformist, Priestley championed the cause of the American colonies and, later, the French Revolution. In 1791 he was run out of Birmingham for his pro-French sentiments, and in 1794 he left Britain for Pennsylvania where both his religion and his political views were more acceptable.

RUMFORD, *Benjamin Thompson, Count, American-British physicist (1753-1814)*

Brilliant, aloof, and egotistical, Count Rumford was a master opportunist. Christened Benjamin Thompson, he experienced lowly beginnings as a storekeeper in Salem, Massachusetts. At nineteen he married a rich widow who was nearly twice his age, and whom he abandoned during the Revolutionary War when he joined the Loyalist cause and left for England. In 1783 he went to

Europe in search of adventure. There he became an administrator for the Elector of Bavaria, was made a count in 1790, and began studying the properties of heat. Producing evidence contrary to Charles Lavoisier's theory of heat as fluid, Rumford advanced the now-accepted theory of heat as a form of energy. In 1799 he returned to England and was acclaimed by the Royal Society, and shortly thereafter founded the Royal Institution. In 1804 he went to Paris, where he married Lavoisier's wealthy widow, former scientific controversies notwithstanding. An unhappy union, they separated four years later, and Rumford spent his last years in Anteuil, where he died at the age of sixty-one, leaving

behind a most checkered personal life, but widespread (and well justified) esteem for his contributions to science.

RUTHERFORD, *Ernest, Lord British physicist (1871-1937)*

Ernest Rutherford is perhaps the single most important man in the evolution of atomic theory. He discovered and named the alpha, beta, and gamma rays; discovered and named the proton; and enunciated the theory of atomic disintegration. He proved that theory by splitting the nucleus of the atom. Born on a New Zealand farm, Rutherford won a Cambridge scholarship in 1895 and began experimenting with radioactive rays shortly after graduation. In 1902, in collaboration with Frederick Soddy, he explained the phenomenon of radioactivity in terms of the breakdown of elements into smaller particles. Rutherford went on to define the nuclear structure of the atom, extending his disintegration theory to the nucleus itself. In 1919 he bombarded a nitrogen atom with alpha particles, penetrating the nucleus and producing the first atomic transmutation. He continued his work in atomic research, was elected president of the Royal Society in 1925, and in 1931 was named Baron of Nelson, after the town of his birth.

STEPHENSON, George, English engineer (1781-1848)

Stephenson's association with railroads developed naturally from his early experience with steam engines. The son of a fireman, Stephenson often helped his father tend the engines used to pump water from the coal mines.

In fact, he even devised a safety lamp for miners at about the same time as Humphry Davy, thus initiating a long controversy as to priority. After studying Watt he began to devise steam engines of his own for use in transportation. In 1815 Stephenson patented a steam locomotive and directed construction of a railway eight miles long to test it. Ten years later he constructed the world's first modern railway, connecting the coal mines of Darlington with

the port of Stockton. It was the first practical passenger railway ever constructed, capable of pulling thirty-eight cars at a speed of twelve to sixteen miles per hour. For the first time land transportation became faster than a galloping horse. He became chief engineer of the Liverpool and Manchester Railway, and directed that line to completion in 1830. His love for the railroad proved constant, and he devoted his entire life to its development. "Let the country make the railways," he once said, "and the railways will make the country."

VOLTA, Alessandro, Italian physicist (1745-1827)

In 1801 Emperor Napoleon summoned Volta to exhibit a strange new electrical device consisting of a series of acid-filled cups connected by zinc and copper-tipped metallic strips. Before an astonished assemblage at the Institute of France, Volta demonstrated the first electric battery. A member of the Royal Society and a professor at the University of Pavia, Volta was a reserved and painstaking man who had been experimenting with electricity for almost three decades. In 1775 he invented the electrophorus, a device for producing charges that is the basis of electrical condensers. A few years later he turned from static electricity to dynamic electricity and began the experiments that led to the discovery of his "Voltaic pile," or battery. He announced his discovery in 1800, and other scientists soon began putting his invention to practical use. Toward the end of his life, after receiving numerous decorations and international acclaim, Volta retired from the world of science and lived in seclusion. But the scientific world did not forget him and named the unit of electromotive force, the volt, in his honor.

WATT, James, Scottish engineer (1736-1819)

The son of a poor Scottish merchant, Watt began his career as an instrument-maker at the University of Glasgow. There he met Joseph Black, the discoverer of latent heat, and together they explored ways of improving the somewhat inefficient steam engine of Thomas Newcomen. In 1765 Watt patented a double-acting engine with separate cylinder and condenser that became the basis for all future steam engines. He then went into business with Matthew Boulton, a Birmingham manufacturer who managed the enterprise to an immediate success. During succeeding years Watt not only continued to improve his engine, but adapted it to a variety of machinery, thus making it an important and versatile source of power. (The watt, a unit of power in the metric system, is named in his honor.) Watt also invented the centrifugal governor to control the steam output of his engines.

WESTINGHOUSE, George American inventor (1846-1914)

"If I understand you, young man, you propose to stop a railroad train with wind; I have no time to listen to such nonsense." That, supposedly, was railway magnate Commodore Vanderbilt's reply to Westinghouse when first presented

with the idea of an air brake. A laggard in school, Westinghouse devoted his mental energies to mechanical inventions. By the age of fifteen he had devised a rotary engine. A few years later he patented his first invention, a railway frog. In 1868, at the age of twenty-two, he produced his revolutionary air brake which made high-speed rail travel safe. He is credited with hundreds of inventions, and was especially influential in the introduction of alternating electric current as a power source. As a businessman the stolid Westinghouse was strong-willed but always regarded as fair. In 1886, in Pittsburgh, he organized Westinghouse Electric Corporation and directed it into an industrial giant.

WHITNEY, *Eli, American inventor (1765-1825)*

"What Peter the Great did to make Russia dominant," wrote Sir Thomas Macauley, "Eli Whitney's invention of the cotton gin has more than equalled in its relation to the power and progress of the United States." Whitney was an inveterate tinkerer whose skill at making contrivances brought him to the attention of a group of wealthy Southerners. In response to their concern with the flagging cotton industry, Whitney designed a machine that could clean the seed from cotton at the rate of fifty pounds a day. In 1793 he patented his invention,

but a series of infringements robbed him of any financial reward. In 1798 he turned to the manufacture of rifles, and this time he made a fortune. Applying the principle of interchangeable parts, Whitney's manufacturing techniques anticipated the era of widespread mass production.

WRIGHT, *Wilbur (1867-1912) and Orville (1871-1948) American inventors.*

On December 17, 1903, the Wright brothers tested their heavier-than-air machine powered by an engine of their own design and construction. Piloted by Orville Wright, the craft remained aloft for twelve seconds, the first airplane flight in history. Their success was witnessed by only five people, and the newspapers greeted their achievement with almost total lack of interest. In fact by 1905 some journals were still calling the Kitty Hawk experiment a fraud. As young men the Wright boys shared strong fraternal bonds and common interests. They even looked alike, having strong, angular faces and probing eyes. In 1892 they turned their considerable mechanical skills to the bicycle repair business in Dayton, Ohio, and later opened their own manufacturing firm. Their interest in flight was sparked by the death of Otto Lilienthal in a glider accident in 1896. The brothers soon constructed their own glider and by 1900 they were soaring more than three hundred feet. After their achievement at Kitty Hawk, the Wrights took their planes on an exhibition tour around Europe. In 1912 Wilbur died of typhoid fever, and his brother became involved in a long and heated dispute with the Smithsonian Institution over whether it was Samuel Langley who actually built the first

heavier-than-air machine. In 1942 Smithsonian officials made a public apology and recognized the Wright claim. The first Wright plane was put on display at the Smithsonian a few years later, and has been among the Institutions most popular attractions ever since.

ZWORYKIN, *Vladimir K. Russian-American physicist (1889-)*

"Ten years ago," wrote Vladimir Zworykin in 1924, "I decided to find a parallel in nature and follow it until I came to television." Zworykin's idea, which he first conceived while studying at the Petrograd Institute of Technology, was to emulate the human eye electronically. Traveling to the United States after World War I, he began to develop his idea at the University of Pittsburgh, where he received a Ph.D. in 1926. There he devised his "iconoscope," the first television pickup tube, and the "kinescope," a receiving tube. By 1929 he had perfected his system and could demonstrate the first practical all-electronic television. That same year Zworykin became director of research at the Radio Corporation of America, where he developed the first electron microscope. Continuing his work in electronics, he introduced a system of color television in 1957.

FURTHER READING

HISTORICAL AND GENERAL

Asimov, Isaac. *The New Intelligent Man's Guide to Science*. New York: Basic Books, Inc., 1965.*

Burlingame, Roger. *Machines That Built America*. New York: Harcourt, Brace & Co., 1953.

Butler, Samuel. *Erewhon*. New York: E.P. Dutton & Co., Inc., 1966.*

Calder, Nigel, ed. *The World in 1984*. Baltimore: Penguin Books, Inc., 1965. 2 Vols.*

Calder, Ritchie. *After the Seventh Day*. New York: Simon and Schuster, Inc., 1961.*

Calder, Ritchie. *Science in our Lives*. rev. ed. New York: The New American Library of World Literature, Inc., 1962.*

De Camp, L. Sprague. *The Ancient Engineers*. Garden City, New York: Doubleday & Company, Inc., 1963.

Derry, T.K., and Williams, Trevor I. *A Short History of Technology*. New York: Oxford University Press, 1961.

Eco, Umberto, and Zorzoli, G.B. *A Pictorial History of Inventions*. New York: The Macmillan Company, 1963.

Finch, James Kip. *The Story of Engineering*. Garden City, New York: Doubleday & Company, Inc., 1960.*

Forbes, R.J., and Dijksterhuis, E.J. *A History of Science and Technology*. Baltimore: Penguin Books, Inc., 1963. 2 Vols. *

Giedion, Siegfried. *Mechanization Takes Command*. New York: Oxford University Press, 1948.

Holbrook, Stewart. *Machines of Plenty: Pioneering in American Agriculture*. New York: The Macmillan Company, 1955.

Kirby, Richard S., and others. *Engineering in History*. New York: McGraw-Hill Book Company, 1956.*

Klemm, Friedrich. *A History of Western Technology*. New York: Charles Scribner's Sons, 1959.*

Kranzberg, Melvin, and Pursell, Carroll W., eds. *Technology in Western Civilization*. New York: Oxford University Press, 1967. 2 Vols.

Lilley, S. *Men, Machines and History*. London: Cobbett Press, 1948.

Lucas, A. *Ancient Egyptian Materials and Industries*. 4th ed. rev. by J.R. Harris. New York: St. Martin's Press, Inc., 1962.

Mantoux, Paul. *The Industrial Revolution in the Eighteenth Century*. New York: Harper & Row, Publishers, 1966.*

Morison, Elting E. *Men, Machines, and Modern Times*. Cambridge: The M.I.T. Press, 1966.

Mumford, Lewis. *Technics and Civilization*. New York: Harcourt, Brace & World, Inc., 1963.*

Mumford, Lewis. *The Myth of the Machine*. New York: Harcourt, Brace & World, Inc., 1966.

Needham, Joseph B. *Science and Civilization in China*. New York: Cambridge University Press, 1966. 4 Vols.

O'Brien, Robert, and the Editors of Life. *Machines*. New York: Time Incorporated, 1964.

Pyke, Magnus. *The Boundaries of Science*. New York: Barnes & Noble, Inc., 1962.*

Singer, Charles, and others, eds. *A History of Technology*. London: Oxford University Press, 1954–1958. 5 Vols.

Soulard, Robert. *A History of the Machine*. New York: Hawthorne Books, Inc., 1963.

Usher, Abbott Payson. *A History of Mechanical Inventions*. Boston: Beacon Press, 1959.*

Wilson, Mitchell. *American Science and Invention*. New York: Simon and Schuster, Inc., 1954.*

Wolf, Abraham. *A History of Science, Technology and Philosophy in the 18th Century*. New York: Harper & Row, Publishers, 1961. 2 Vols.*

Wolf, Abraham. *A History of Science, Technology, and Philosophy in the 16th and 17th Centuries*. New York: Harper & Row, Publishers, 1959. 2 Vols.*

SPECIALIZED FIELDS

Bitter, Francis. *Magnets*. Garden City, New York: Doubleday & Company, Inc., 1959.*

Brotherton, M. *Masers and Lasers*. New York: McGraw-Hill Book Company, 1964.

Calder, Ritchie. *Living with the Atom*. Chicago: University of Chicago Press, 1962.

Chalmers, Bruce. *Energy*. New York: Academic Press Inc., 1963.

Fink, Donald G. *Computers and the Human Mind*. Garden City, New York: Doubleday & Company, Inc., 1966.*

Fishlock, David. *A Guide to the Laser*. London: MacDonald & Co., 1967.

Glasstone, Samuel. *Sourcebook on Atomic Energy*. Princeton, New Jersey: D. Van Nostrand Co., Inc., 1958.

Hilton, Alice Mary. *Logic, Computing Machines and Automation*. Cleveland: The World Publishing Company, 1964.*

Kursh, Harry. *Inside the U.S. Patent Office*. New York: W.W. Norton & Company, Inc., 1959.

Laithwaite, E.R. *Propulsion Without Wheels*. London: The English Universities Press, Ltd., 1966.

Lapp, Ralph E. *Roads to Discovery*. New York: Harper & Row, Publishers, 1960.

Lee, Eric W. *Magnetism*. Baltimore: Penguin Books, Inc., 1963.*

Page, Robert Morris. *The Origin of Radar*. Garden City, New York: Doubleday & Company, Inc., 1962.*

Sharlin, Harold I. *The Making of the Electrical Age*. New York: Abelard-Schuman, Ltd., 1963.

Taylor, F.S. *A History of Industrial Chemistry*. London: William Heinemann, Ltd., 1957.

Uhbelohde, A.R. *Man and Energy*. London: Hutchinson & Co., 1954.

Wiener, Norbert. *Cybernetics*. New York: John Wiley & Sons, Inc., 1948.*

Wiener, Norbert. *The Human Use of Human Beings*. 2nd rev. ed. New York: Houghton Mifflin Company, 1954.*

BIOGRAPHY

Andrade, E.N. da C. *Rutherford and the Nature of the Atom*. Garden City, New York: Doubleday & Company, Inc., 1964.*

Brown, Sanborn C. *Count Rumford*. Garden City, New York: Doubleday & Company, Inc., 1962.*

Dickenson, Henry W., and Jenkins, R. *James Watt and the Steam Engine*. London: Oxford University Press, 1927.

Fuller, Edmund. *Tinkers and Genius*. New York: Hastings House, Publishers, Inc., 1955.

Green, Constance M. *Eli Whitney and the Birth of American Technology*. Boston: Little, Brown & Company, 1956.*

Hughes, Thomas P., ed. *Lives of the Engineers*. Cambridge, Massachusetts: The M.I.T. Press, 1966.

Josephson, Matthew. *Edison*. New York: McGraw-Hill Book Company, 1963.*

Lehman, Milton. *This High Man*. New York: Farrar, Strauss, & Company, 1963.

MacDonald, D.K.C. *Faraday, Maxwell, and Kelvin*. Garden City, New York: Doubleday & Company, Inc., 1964.*

Mirsky, Jeannette, and Nevins, Allan. *The World of Eli Whitney*. New York: Collier Books, 1962.*

Nevins, Allan. *Ford: The Times, The Man, The Company*. New York: Charles Scribner's Sons, 1954.

Schofield, Robert E. *The Lunar Society of Birmingham*. New York: Oxford University Press, 1963.

Van Doren, Carl. *Benjamin Franklin*. New York: The Viking Press, 1966.*

Available in paperback.

INDEX

Italics indicate illustrations

A NOTE ON THIS BOOK

This book was published by the Editors of American Heritage Publishing Company in association with the Smithsonian Institution under the following editorial direction: For the Smithsonian Institution, Anders Richter, Director, Smithsonian Institution Press. For American Heritage, Editor, David G. McCullough; Art Director, Jack Newman; Assistant Art Director, Donald Longabucco; Copy Editor, Bill Hansen; Assistant Editors, Maria Ealand and Gay Sherry; Picture Editor, Martha F. Grossman; Editorial Assistants, Nancy Kelly, Susan J. Lewis, Nancy Lindemeyer, and Karen Olstad.

PICTURE CREDITS